Creative S.

A Woman's Guide To Becoming An Erotic
Enchantress Of Superlustful Sex

Revised 2012

Nannette LaRee Hernandez

Author's Raison D'être:

The Human Male is **genetically programmed** to hunger and hunt for sex: first, middle, last, at all times, perpetually and forever.

This book is accurately and factually detailed about your man and his Brain-Sex and it is brutally straightforward, with candid truths and licentious information, all about sex from a male perspective.

How **your** man desires Sex.

Wants Sex.

Craves Sex.

Needs Sex.

How he wants **you** to fuck **him**.

You will never understand your man and what he desires better than you will after reading It here.

The Author

Creative Screwing:
A Woman's Guide to Becoming an Erotic Enchantress of Superlustful
Sex
Revised & Expanded 2012

By Nannette LaRee Hernandez

ISBN 978-1-105-49934-0

Siento Sordida
Madison WI
https://sites.google.com/site/sientosordida/

Dedication

With appreciation and dedication to: Cleopatra, Mata Hari, Anais Nin, Marie Carmichael Stopes, Margaret Sanger, Annie Sprinkle, Betty Dodson and Carrie, Miranda, Charlotte and Samantha, those great gals from Sex & the City... fearless, audacious women whom I admire; women who all experienced the power of their sexuality, and lived much better lives because of it.

Well Behaved Women Rarely Make History.

Disclaimer I:

I've written this book in 'Man Speak', using sexual terminology cut-straight from your man's male vocabulary: cock, pussy, balls, ass, fuck... all those naughty words you were once taught to never, ever say.

I've also featured numerous writings from other exceptional sex experts and relationship authors, as well as erotic pictures, photographs and illustrations from many gifted artists and raunchy venues on the internet; all which graphically demonstrate and reveal how your man desires and visualizes sex.

You are fucking a man.

This requires **that you must** interpret sex **exactly** the way your man thinks it, sees it, feels it, wants it and eds it - if you desire a successful romantic relationship w im.

If you don't desire a truly successful romantic ationship with your man, read someone else's book.

Nannette LaRee

Disclaimer II:

This work is solely the product of the efforts of the Author. The Editorial Staff and Publisher have made no effort to verify the facts and statements contained in this work. All claims, facts and statements expressed in this work are solely the responsibility of the Author, and neither the Editors nor the Publisher accept any responsibility or liability for these remarks or the consequences thereof.

Disclaimer III:

This work is intended for entertainment purposes only. All other uses are solely at the discretion and on the responsibility of the reader.

The Contents:

*Let there be pleasure on earth
and let it begin with me.*

~~~Annie Sprinkle

yoursexualpoweryoursexualpoweryoursexualpoweryoursexualpoweryours
exualpoweryoursexualpoweryoursexualpoweryoursexualpoweryoursexual
poweryoursexualpoweryoursexualpoweryoursexualpoweryoursexualpower
yoursexualpoweryoursexualpoweryoursexualpoweryoursexualpoweryours
exualpoweryoursexualpoweryoursexualpoweryoursexualpoweryoursexual
poweryoursexualpoweryoursexualpoweryoursexualpoweryoursexualpower
yoursexualpoweryoursexualpoweryoursexualpoweryoursexualpoweryours
exualpoweryoursexualpoweryoursexualpoweryoursexualpoweryoursexual
poweryoursexualpoweryoursexualpoweryoursexualpoweryoursexualpower
yoursexualpoweryoursexualpoweryoursexualpoweryoursexualpoweryours
exualpoweryoursexualpoweryoursexualpoweryoursexualpoweryoursexual

Why Adam Ate That Apple

poweryoursexualpoweryoursexualpoweryoursexualpoweryoursexualpower
yoursexualpoweryoursexualpoweryoursexualpoweryoursexualpoweryours
exualpoweryoursexualpoweryoursexualpoweryoursexualpoweryoursexual
poweryoursexualpoweryoursexualpoweryoursexualpoweryoursexualpower
yoursexualpoweryoursexualpoweryoursexualpoweryoursexualpoweryours
exualpoweryoursexualpoweryoursexualpoweryoursexualpoweryoursexual
poweryoursexualpoweryoursexualpoweryoursexualpoweryoursexualpower
yoursexualpoweryoursexualpoweryoursexualpoweryoursexualpoweryours
exualpoweryoursexualpoweryoursexualpoweryoursexualpoweryoursexual
poweryoursexualpoweryoursexualpoweryoursexualpoweryoursexualpower
yoursexualpoweryoursexualpoweryoursexualpoweryoursexualpoweryours
exualpoweryoursexualpoweryoursexualpoweryoursexualpoweryoursexual
poweryoursexualpoweryoursexualpoweryoursexualpoweryoursexualpower
yoursexualpoweryoursexualpoweryoursexualpoweryoursexualpoweryours
exualpoweryoursexualpoweryoursexualpoweryoursexualpoweryoursexual
poweryoursexualpoweryoursexualpoweryoursexualpoweryoursexualpower
yoursexualpoweryoursexualpoweryoursexualpoweryoursexualpoweryours
exualpoweryoursexualpoweryoursexualpoweryoursexualpoweryoursexual
poweryoursexualpoweryoursexualpoweryoursexualpoweryoursexualpower
yoursexualpoweryoursexualpoweryoursexualpoweryoursexualpoweryours
exualpoweryoursexualpoweryoursexualpoweryoursexualpoweryoursexual
poweryoursexualpoweryoursexualpoweryoursexualpoweryoursexualpower
yoursexualpoweryoursexualpoweryoursexualpoweryoursexualpoweryours
exualpoweryoursexualpoweryoursexualpoweryoursexualpoweryoursexual
poweryoursexualpoweryoursexualpoweryoursexualpoweryoursexualpower
yoursexualpoweryoursexualpoweryoursexualpoweryoursexualpoweryours
exualpoweryoursexualpoweryoursexualpoweryoursexualpoweryoursexual
poweryoursexualpoweryoursexualpoweryoursexualpoweryoursexualpower
yoursexualpoweryoursexualpoweryoursexualpoweryoursexualpoweryours
exualpoweryoursexualpoweryoursexualpoweryoursexualpoweryoursexual
poweryoursexualpoweryoursexualpoweryoursexualpoweryoursexualpower
yoursexualpoweryoursexualpoweryoursexualpoweryoursexualpoweryours
exualpoweryoursexualpoweryoursexualpoweryoursexualpoweryoursexual
poweryoursexualpoweryoursexualpoweryoursexualpoweryoursexualpower
yoursexualpoweryoursexualpoweryoursexualpoweryoursexualpoweryours
exualpoweryoursexualpoweryoursexualpoweryoursexualpoweryoursexual
poweryoursexualpoweryoursexualpoweryoursexualpoweryoursexualpower
yoursexualpoweryoursexualpoweryoursexualpoweryoursexualpoweryours
exualpoweryoursexualpoweryoursexualpoweryoursexualpoweryoursexual

I. Why Adam Ate That Apple

*So long has the myth of feminine inferiority prevailed,
that women themselves find it hard to believe
that their own sex was once and for a very long time,
the superior and dominant sex.*

~~~Elizabeth Gould Davis

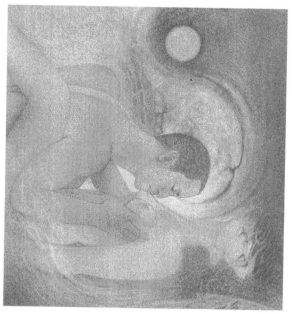

Artwork featured at: www.secretgardenpublishing.com

In the year 1917, Marie Carmichael Stopes, authoress of the book '*Married Love*', declared to the world: *"In my own marriage I paid such a terrible price for sex-ignorance that I feel that knowledge gained at such a terrible cost should be placed at the service of humanity."*

Marie Carmichael Stopes was a Doctor of Science and Philosophy and a Fellow of the Royal Society of Literature, as well as the London Linnean Society. Yet, for all her education and impressive recognition throughout Europe, her personal life was miserable because of her naive ignorance regarding the sexual mind and sexual desires of the man she had wed. We are now living in the 21st

Century, and most women are still as ignorant about the sexual perspective and sexual desires of their man, as women were in the year 1917.

You might feel that much of what you read here is offensively blunt and tactlessly direct. It needs to be. My objective is that you will use the uncharted information you read in my book to understand and acknowledge your man's sexual perspective, and then utilize what you've learned to disburse your sexual power and create genuine lust and passion within your romantic relationship.

Up to this moment in your romantic relationship, you've always fucked your man from your female perspective, and so you do not understand your man or who he is, what he wants, what he needs, or what he feels... because you've never taken into consideration how different his sexual perspective is from yours, and you've never made an effort to 'get' his genetically ingrained Sexual Biology.

So, let me explain the Importance of Sex and how your man sees it:

If every woman took pleasure in running her tongue from her man's neck to his cock, and if every woman made an effort to comprehend the Brain-Sex *of her man and therefore his genetic Nucleus-pull to gawk at bare breasts, there would be unconditional Harmony on Planet Earth.*

Yes. It is that simple, and that matter-of-fact. Men are not complicated creatures.

Men are simplistic creations without any want, need or desire for domestication or civilization.

Left on their own (and, therefore, undomesticated), men would masturbate as a job title. They would run wildly in man-packs throughout the streets, pausing only to take a piss, snatch a bite to eat, and get laid.

This genre of behavior is the *Biology of Man*, and because you are fucking a man, it's crucial in your romantic relationship with him that you repetitively approach sex with him from his perspective, because sooner or later most men do want to settle into a safe and stable romantic-environment, since most men enjoy the regularity of having their ass licked and their cock sucked by an owner who feeds them top-quality food and gives them an endless amount of affection.

To really keep any man (getting him is easy, it's the keeping him part that is complicated), you've got to break your female sex-ruler and stop judging him by your pussy-emotions. What works for you sexually does not work for him, and if you refuse to apply this valuable information to your romantic relationship, then you will never really hold onto your man... he will eternally be on the sniff-out for that one woman who will truly "get him."

I average about 400 emails a month from women who revere Dr. Phil and write to me for advice on my website www.sensualseductress.com, because of my public notice which is posted on the Sex/Relationship message boards on www.DrPhil.com.

In one letter that I answered and posted, I offered some shrewd advice to a woman by taking my cue from the clever book *How To Make Your Man Behave In 21 Days Or Less: Using The Secrets Of Professional Dog Trainers*, written by Karen Salmansohn. It wasn't long before an irate male reader at www.DrPhil.com chastised me because I had referred to men as dogs. So, I gently replied to the guy with this: "What is essential to a Dog's survival is exactly what is essential to a Man's survival:

1) Dog's Bone:(Man's Penis)

2) Dog's Bowl:(Man's Food)

3) Dog's Ball:(Man's Big Boy Toys)

4) Dog's Nap:(Man's Sleep)

5) Dog's pissing In Other People's Yards:(Man's need to be in Control, mark his territory, establish Male dominance)

6) Dog's Sniffing Butts:(Man's Sniffing after Women)

The irate guy never bothered to answer or argue back ~ but numerous men who posted a response in return, completely agreed with me!

In the book *The Bastard on the Couch*, edited by Daniel Jones, guest author Vince Passaro clarifies the similarity between men and dogs in his essay *"Why Men Lie and Always Will"*: *"My wife especially loved (our male dog); he signified everything she actually likes about men: he was relentlessly exuberant and strong, and in his tremendous eagerness to get to the next thing he used to literally pull her over when she was walking him. The crucial point was that she was able to enjoy his generally compulsive, single-minded, uncooperative and relentlessly horny nature because she associated him with none of the disappointed social expectations or emotional pain that she associated with actual human males, such as me. I envied him!"*

What Vince Passaro proves in that one paragraph, is that men have been behaving like compulsive, single-minded, uncooperative, relentlessly horny beasts since the Beginning of Time because that is how men are *Genetically Programmed*... and no booming Feminist March on Washington or any Act of Equality that is passed by Congress, will ever, ever change that Biological Fact.

And neither will you.

To quote Dr. Phil: *"... you can't fix what you won't acknowledge!"* Since that statement is Testament, you'd better believe that you will never, ever have the romantic relationship you want with your man if you refuse to accept his DNA, his Biology, and his Genetic Programming to *just get fucked* anywhere, anyhow and anytime he can.

Preferably with you... but, then, that depends on how you behave toward him in the bedroom.

The naughtiest book ever written is *The Bible*, and there is enough filth in that book to denigrate entire nations – and it has. What's more, *The Bible* is an all-inclusive blueprint to the absolute simplicity of the Male Mind: *Man wants pussy so badly he's willing to defy God and relinquish ownership of an entire Planet for it*. It's been this way since Adam first met Eve!

So... the next time you feel that your man has behaved like a dog because he purchased online-porn while you were out-of-town... just remember that Adam voluntarily turned his back on God and got his ass kicked-out of The Garden of Eden, all for another plummet into Eve's secret garden. There is so much evidence of what men have done for sex, it would take a decade to research all the Historical specifics of how much men have lost and how low men have gone, just for the *vague promise* of pussy!

Whether your opinion is that it's Creation or a Fairytale story... you know that Adam ate that apple. Adam chose Eve's pussy over God, the Garden of Eden, and all the control he had over every single living thing on Planet Earth. Adam behaved just like the horny male beasts in the field - all hail to the Power of the Pussy.

Your pussy is the most valuable commodity ever created, invented, dreamed-of, or produced.

You are the superior and dominant sex.
In this book, I will show you the advantage you need to have the romantic relationship you've always wanted with your man, as well as the entitlement to enjoy, relish, fantasize, savor, devour, desire and fuck your man with all the supremacy and passion that has belonged to you and that has existed in your genetic programming and DNA, since Eve first offered Adam that apple.

nakedbootieshandjobsdirtydancingbarebreastsblowjobsnakedbootiesha
ndjobsdirtydancingbarebreastsblowjobsnakedbootieshandjobsdirtydan
cingbarebreastsblowjobsnakedbootieshandjobsdirtydancingbarebreast
sblowjobsnakedbootieshandjobsdirtydancingbarebreastsblowjobsnaked
bootieshandjobsdirtydancingbarebreastsblowjobsnakedbootieshandjob
sdirtydancingbarebreastsblowjobsnakedbootieshandjobsdirtydancingb
arebreastsblowjobsnakedbootieshandjobsdirtydancingbarebreastsblow
jobsnakedbootieshandjobsdirtydancingbarebreastsblowjobsnakedbooti
eshandjobsdirtydancingbarebreastsblowjobsnakedbootieshandjobsdirt
ydancingbarebreastsblowjobsnakedbootieshandjobsdirtydancingbarebr
eastsblowjobsnakedbootieshandjobsdirtydancingbarebreastsblowjobsn
akedbootieshandjobsdirtydancingbarebreastsblowjobsnakedbootieshan
Djobsdirtydancingbarebreastsblowjobsnakedbootieshandjobsdirtydanc
ingbarebreastsblowjobsnakedbootieshandjobsdirtydancingbarebreasts

What Your Man
Desires... Wants... Needs

blowjobsnakedbootieshandjobsdirtydancingbarebreastsblowjobsnakedb
ootieshandjobsdirtydancingbarebreastsblowjobsnakedbootieshandjobs
dirtydancingbarebreastsblowjobsnakedbootieshandjobsdirtydancingba
rebreastsblowjobsnakedbootieshandjobsdirtydancingbarebreastsblowj
obsnakedbootieshandjobsdirtydancingbarebreastsblowjobsnakedbootie
shandjobsdirtydancingbarebreastsblowjobsnakedbootieshandjobsdirty
dancingbarebreastsblowjobsnakedbootieshandjobsdirtydancingbarebre
astsblowjobsnakedbootieshandjobsdirtydancingbarebreastsblowjobsna
kedbootieshandjobsdirtydancingbarebreastsblowjobsnakedbootieshand
jobsdirtydancingbarebreastsblowjobsnakedbootieshandjobsdirtydanci
ngbarebreastsblowjobsnakedbootieshandjobsdirtydancingbarebreastsb
lowjobsnakedbootieshandjobsdirtydancingbarebreastsblowjobsnakedbo
otieshandjobsdirtydancingbarebreastsblowjobsnakedbootieshandjobsd
irtydancingbarebreastsblowjobsnakedbootieshandjobsdirtydancingbar
ebreastsblowjobsnakedbootieshandjobsdirtydancingbarebreastsblowjo
bsnakedbootieshandjobsdirtydancingbarebreastsblowjobsnakedbooties
handjobsdirtydancingbarebreastsblowjobsnakedbootieshandjobsdirtyd
ancingbarebreastsblowjobsnakedbootieshandjobsdirtydancingbarebrea
stsblowjobsnakedbootieshandjobsdirtydancingbarebreastsblowjobsnak
edbootieshandjobsdirtydancingbarebreastsblowjobsnakedbootieshandj
obsdirtydancingbarebreastsblowjobsnakedbootieshandjobsdirtydancin
gbarebreastsblowjobsnakedbootieshandjobsdirtydancingbarebreastsbl
owjobsnakedbootieshandjobsdirtydancingbarebreastsblowjobsnakedboo
tieshandjobsdirtydancingbarebreastsblowjobsnakedbootieshandjobsdi
rtydancingbarebreastsblowjobsnakedbootieshandjobsdirtydancingbare
breastsblowjobsnakedbootieshandjobsdirtydancingbarebreastsblowjob
snakedbootieshandjobsdirtydancingbarebreastsblowjobsnakedbootiesh
andjobsdirtydancingbarebreastsblowjobsnakedbootieshandjobsdirtyda
ncingbarebreastsblowjobsnakedbootieshandjobsdirtydancingbarebreas
tsblowjobsnakedbootieshandjobsdirtydancingbarebreastsblowjobsnake
dbootieshandjobsdirtydancingbarebreastsblowjobsnakedbootieshandjo
bsdirtydancingbarebreastsblowjobsnakedbootieshanDjobsdirtydancing
barebreastsblowjobsnakedbootieshandjobsdirtydancingbarebreastsblo
wjobsnakedbootieshandjobsdirtydancingbarebreastsblowjobsnakedboot
ieshandjobsdirtydancingbarebreastsblowjobsnakedbootieshandjobsdir
tydancingbarebreastsblowjobsnakedbootieshandjobsdirtydancingbareb
reastsblowjobsnakedbootieshandjobsdirtydancingbarebreastsblowjobs
nakedbootieshandjobsdirtydancingbarebreastsblowjobsnakedbootiesha
ndjobsdirtydancingbarebreastsblowjobsnakedbootieshandjobsdirtydan

II. What Your Man Desires, Wants & Needs

*Careful about making alterations when it comes to men...
one pull of the wrong thread and the whole thing falls
apart. You can't change a man.*

~~~Samantha, in Sex and the City

Artwork featured at: www.gradiva.com/

The blatant evidence of what men desire, want and need, has been around since Adam took that apple from Eve: Man is obsessed with having, hunting, obtaining, chasing and getting pussy.

Face it: if the story reads that the First Man to ever step foot on Planet Earth gave it all up for pussy---did you actually think your man was 'different'?

When it comes to sex, It is what It is: your man *will never evolve or ever become enlightened* past his desire, want and need for pussy.

Pussy.

You should repeat that word over and over like a mantra until your brain conclusively accepts the obvious about your man. *It is obvious.*

From wet t-shirt contests at the beach to tempting women who dance topless at strip clubs... X-rated porn theaters and triple XXX videos/DVD's that sell in the billions... nudie magazines where naked women masturbate in orgasmic bliss or hungrily suckle on a man's cock... erotic massage parlors, peep booths, private lingerie modeling, millions of subscriptions to online porn, the on-going existence of prostitution and of extra-marital affairs... each and every one of these factors give a clear indication of what men desire, want and need sexually. It has never been a secret or a mystery what your man desires, wants and needs. More-than-likely, you've chosen (or even been taught) to ignore it as if it were a flu bug that he'll eventually "get over."

There's no "getting over it" for him.

Ever.

You cannot ignore, demand, scream, guilt, blame, push, bully, convince, manipulate, pray, insist or force that desire, want and need for pussy out of him.

While one man's fantasies will vary from another's, all men desire The Supreme Fantasy: a woman who is sexually open-minded and pays attention to what turns him on. Any woman who is frequently provocative and takes charge in the bedroom while using her sexual imagination... and any woman who talks dirty to him while she is willingly exploratory and passionate, will positively curb his lustful male appetite for naked dancing ladies and Internet pussy.

I didn't say "take away" a man's appetite for outside entertainment... however a sexually-charged woman will definitely curb and practically cure that appetite! When a man gets a sexual smorgasbord at home, then any naked woman he can't have, can't touch or can't keep, is like having to dine on a stale hamburger at a bus stop.

I receive copious amounts of email from women who complain about the fact that men just seem to want sex. There is no "seem" about it: sex is exactly what men want, and everything else that a man does, from driving his car to doing his job, all derive directly from what he and his cock want: SEX.

Because a man is really two people: Himself, and His Cock. A man's cock is the Alpha Male in *that* relationship!

The entire point of this book is to take you inside the mind of your man so that you will finally understand sex from his level and see sex as he sees it... so that with this power and knowledge you can completely revolutionize and revise your romantic relationship with him.

If you refuse to accept the truth about men or about your man... you will never ever have the romantic relationship that you desire, want and need with him.

Ever.

cockinformationcockinformationcockinformationcockinformationcocki
nformationcockinformationcockinformationcockinformationcockinform
ationcockinformationcockinformationcockinformationcockinformation
cockinformationcockinformationcockinformationcockinformationcocki
nformationcockinformationcockinformationcockinformationcockinform
ationcockinformationcockinformationcockinformationcockinformation
cockinformationcockinformationcockinformationcockinformationcocki
nformationcockinformationcockinformationcockinformationcockinform
ationcockinformationcockinformationcockinformationcockinformation
cockinformationcockinformationcockinformationcockinformationcocki
nformationcockinformationcockinformationcockinformationcockinform
ationcockinformationcockinformationcockinformationcockinformation

Your Man's Personal Playmate

cockinformationcockinformationcockinformationcockinformationcocki
nformationcockinformationcockinformationcockinformationcockinform
ationcockinformationcockinformationcockinformationcockinformation
cockinformationcockinformationcockinformationcockinformationcocki
nformationcockinformationcockinformationcockinformationcockinform
ationcockinformationcockinformationcockinformationcockinformation
cockinformationcockinformationcockinformationcockinformationcocki
nformationcockinformationcockinformationcockinformationcockinform
ationcockinformationcockinformationcockinformationcockinformation
cockinformationcockinformationcockinformationcockinformationcocki
nformationcockinformationcockinformationcockinformationcockinform
ationcockinformationcockinformationcockinformationcockinformation
cockinformationcockinformationcockinformationcockinformationcocki
nformationcockinformationcockinformationcockinformationcockinform
ationcockinformationcockinformationcockinformationcockinformation
cockinformationcockinformationcockinformationcockinformationcocki
nformationcockinformationcockinformationcockinformationcockinform
ationcockinformationcockinformationcockinformationcockinformation
cockinformationcockinformationcockinformationcockinformationcocki
nformationcockinformationcockinformationcockinformationcockinform
ationcockinformationcockinformationcockinformationcockinformation
cockinformationcockinformationcockinformationcockinformationcocki
nformationcockinformationcockinformationcockinformationcockinform
ationcockinformationcockinformationcockinformationcockinformation
cockinformationcockinformationcockinformationcockinformationcocki
nformationcockinformationcockinformationcockinformationcockinform
ationcockinformationcockinformationcockinformationcockinformation
cockinformationcockinformationcockinformationcockinformationcocki
nformationcockinformationcockinformationcockinformationcockinform
ationcockinformationcockinformationcockinformationcockinformation
cockinformationcockinformationcockinformationcockinformationcocki
nformationcockinformationcockinformationcockinformationcockinform
ationcockinformationcockinformationcockinformationcockinformation
cockinformationcockinformationcockinformationcockinformationcocki
nformationcockinformationcockinformationcockinformationcockinform
ationcockinformationcockinformationcockinformationcockinformation
cockinformationcockinformationcockinformationcockinformationcocki
nformationcockinformationcockinformationcockinformationcockinform

III. Your Man's Personal Playmate

A man is two people: Himself, and his Cock.

~~~Beryl Bainbridge

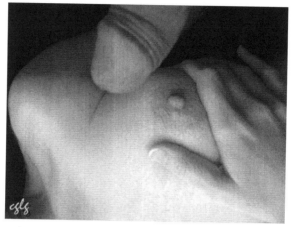

Artist CGLG Artwork featured at: www.eroticalee.com

You are not his best friend.

His cock is.

It is neither possible nor probable that you will *ever, ever* understand the relationship that your man has with his cock, but you'd better acknowledge that committed relationship because everything your man does revolves around his cock and you need to have a very close and intimate relationship with his cock if you're ever going to be "in the loop."

Your man's cock is everything to him from his personal playmate to his justifiable excuse for the numerous screwed-up things that he does, and most of your man's personal worth and how he views himself is directly connected to his cock.

Once again: do not try and figure this out ~ you never, ever will. Just breathe in, let it go and accept your man's cock for what it is: his personal playmate, his very best buddy and his Enigmatic Center.

Now that you've conceded to whom your man's best friend really is, *never, ever ignore your man's cock*. Make sure that you persistently pay attention to him and touch him where it counts: his cock.

I cannot put enough emphasis on this: *be user-friendly with your man's cock*. Admire it. Play with it. Kiss it. Fondle it. Revere it. Appreciate it. Worship it.

~One-Size Cock Does Fit All~

Watch any John Wayne film and who you see is a tough, confident man that embodies a woman's idea of a rugged and sexy hero; what's more, John Wayne was the same man in everyday life that he personified on camera.

John Wayne had a 3-inch penis when it was erect.

Given this Historical Fact (with many thanks to '*The Penis Book*,' by Joseph Cohen), it's pretty obvious that a man's sexiness and magnitude have nothing what-so-ever to do with the size of his cock. The author recommends that you buy Joseph Cohen's book; the man is a penis expert!

50% of all men have a 5.9-inch cock when erect, and two-thirds of the remaining 50% of all men measure between 5.1 to 6.2 inches when their cock is erect.

That leaves a very small percentage of men who have less-than average or larger-than average cocks.

African American men have the largest cocks, Caucasian men's cocks come in second and Asian men have the smallest cocks; *however*, the Kama Sutra was written by an Asian man - which is further proof that the biggest sex organ is a man's brain. So, there's at least some evidence that one man figured that out!

Stats aside though, how your man feels about his cock truthfully depends on how you treat him, because it is also true that a number of men with extra-large cocks have just as much anxiety as men with average and smaller cocks.

Several of the world's most famous male porn stars have spoken-out about the embarrassment they've endured from women they'd dated or married who treated their cocks like a deformity because of the enormous size.

It's really amazing how much a man's opinion of himself is contingent on his cock for soooooo many anomalous reasons.

When I first self-published this book in 1993, I was in New York to tape *Real Personal with Bob Berkowitz* on CNBC. Many other TV-talk shows heard that I was in town and I ended-up promoting my book on numerous TV programs as well as meeting several Hollywood stars and famous media personalities.

One night I went clubbing in SoHo with a boisterous group from MTV, and one of the girls who worked as an executive's assistant spilled the best celebrity sex gossip I've ever heard!

This gal named to me over a dozen film stars and pro athletes she'd slept with, including an A-List 4-star celebrity she had fucked several years earlier while he was filming a movie in New York who, she'd told me, (quote) *"... (he) was lucky if his scrawny cock was five inches hard... and he is still the best fuck I've ever had, as of 12:17 AM this morning! He fucked me in my ass and fingered my clit at the same time so good, that when I came, I felt my head was going to pop right off my neck! I came so much, it squeezed all the fluid out of me ~ I even peed (on) my bed!"*

So now, whenever I see that actor in a movie, I appreciate that all the hot-n-sexy he gives-off on screen is who he really is, and not at all based on the size of his cock. And that one simple Know just makes me feel so much sweeter about men and the relationship each one has with his cock. This is probably why I'm such an oral girl!

In the Third Season of *Sex and The City*, Samantha dates a man whom she tells the girls is wonderful in every way, except for his "tiny little dick" and the fact that she "... can't feel it!" when he fucks her. A few weeks later, the relationship ends with Samantha dumping the poor guy *because, and only because*, of his tiny little dick. After that episode aired, I had lunch with a few of my girlfriends who'd also watched the episode, and it was the general consensus round the table that *Sex and The City* had confirmed that a man's cock size does matter to a woman's sexual fulfillment! When I suggested that perhaps the guy's cock was really too small for the lovely but promiscuous Samantha because her pussy was probably stretched-out Grand Canyon Style from all the men she'd fucked, it at least gave my friends another perspective to consider! What's so funny, is later that season, Samantha begins dating a man whose cock is "too big" and the scene between her and Carrie goes like this:

Samantha: "You dated Mr. Big. I'm dating Mr. Too-Big!"

Carrie: "You broke up with your last boyfriend because he was too small, now this one's too big. Who are you, Goldie-Cocks?"

Samantha: "Yep! I'm looking for one that's juuuust right."

Which proves when you meet your Just Right guy, the size of his cock is a crap shoot... so please take the following into consideration the next time a man unzips, and you are presented with an extra-small or an extra-large cock... because it is *who* He is, a man with small heart or a big heart, that is what will matter most at the end of the day.

~Size Matters~

If you are single and you're with a man who is a really great guy and has a lot to offer you, but his cock is just 'too average' or just 'too below average' in your eyes, you might want to consider that: A) perhaps your pussy is just too stretched and you should begin doing some vaginal-tightening kegal exercises *and then* reconsider your opinion of him. Or B) in all probability, your brain is just too small and you can't see the quality of who he is for all the hyped-up bigger-is-better bullshit you've been inculturated to believe about the size of a man's cock.

This same point applies if you feel that his cock is too enormous to cum into your pussy-party, let alone cum in your mouth; you've got to consider *all* the options before you make-up your mind and ruin your opportunity for a great romantic relationship all based on a cock-technicality.

If you're in a committed relationship and your man's cock is far-below or way-above average size, chances are you already know he has some anxiety about it and that in his past relationships, he is sure to have been with at least one woman who didn't treat him right just because his cock was too small or too big in her judgment, and she let him know it. Men often have the annoying tendency to apply what a woman in their past has said or done to the new woman they are with. This means you will constantly and continually need to re-inforce how sexy you feel he is, because no man can hear those words enough and what it takes to get him to really believe it would take a whole other book, so your best bet is to *just be consistent*.

Any woman who dumps a wonderful man or treats him without sexual respect because of the size of his cock, whether she feels he is just too big or just too small, is the exact definition of an idiot.

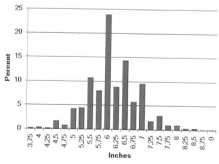

Here is a chart comparing penis lengths of an average penis size. As you can see from the chart, the average penis size is 6 inches.

www.sexual-compare.com

~Sexy Moves If He Is...~

The most common dilemma that every Internet Sex Expert receives from men, are letter-emails that convey: "... my penis is too small" or "... my penis is too big."

In college, my second boyfriend was a Paul Bunyan of a man with a very small cock. I honestly wasn't sure how to talk with him about it. There was no way I was going to make a mistake and say anything that might hurt him... and when I went to the bookstore seeking help with my problem, there were no books written advising me what to do. So, I originated some creative sex-moves where I could 'feel' it better. Once I allowed my sexually creative imagination loose, not only could I 'feel it' more, but the sex became more memorable than with other boyfriends down the line whose cocks were average and above. In contrast to my dilemma, a classmate of mine had the opposite problem: her boyfriend had a very big cock and it hurt her every time they had intercourse. Our '*Anatomy and Physiology*' class was taught by a minute German professor who, though brilliant, was a real bore. Janna and I sat at the back of the classroom and gained a real education from each other as we discovered skillful ways to improve our sex with our men.

Any woman can make her man's cock work to her advantage; all she has to do is want to.

If His Cock is too Small:

Sex Move #1:

A) Corner yourself on the side of your bed, against the wall. If your bed isn't against the wall, move it there.

B) Use a large, firm pillow underneath your lower back and a medium, very firm pillow underneath your buttocks or go to website: www.liberator.com, and purchase one of their sex-specialty pillow-ramps.

C) When he gets inside of you, just lift your legs and slide them over his shoulders. You will 'feel' it.

Sex Move #2:

A) Place a small very plump and firm pillow, mid-bed. Or you can purchase specialty pillows from www.liberator.com.

B) Lay face-down on the bed, flat, with your lower tummy resting elevated-up on the pillow.

c) Keep your legs closed together.

D) Have him straddle you and enter you, with your legs closed.

Sex Move #3:

A) Place a folded, comfortable velvet blanket on the floor.

B) Sit him on the floor, against the bed, couch, or a solid reclining chair, with his legs out and slightly spread.

C) Now sit on top of him, and slide his cock inside of you.

D) Ask him to bring his legs up, so that your back can lean and rest against them.

E) Lean back against his legs until your pussy is tilted against his lower tummy and you can rub your clit against his tummy.

F) Ride him bronco-style by thrusting your hips back-and-forth in short moves, then circling your hips in figure-8's without much movement, in long-winding moves.

If His Cock is too Big:

1) Test out the best lubricants and find the one that gives his cock the most "slide and glide" when he is inside of you. After you've found the best lubricant, make sure that you always use lots and lots of lubrication when you have intercourse with him. This will make the thrust less-painful and much smoother. If that means you need to invest in an expensive lube, then do so.

2) Spend time on becoming sexually aroused before you have intercourse with him, because if his cock is too big for you, you know when It's coming and this causes extra

tension and tautness in your lower extremities, as well as your entire being. *This is a situation where knowing your own body is a Must.* So, A) If he's isn't home yet you can masturbate alone and this will relax your body and release most of your tension. Or, B) Right before you and he have intercourse, if he gives you oral sex or uses his hands to make you come before he enters you, this will also fully relax the tension in your body, and your whole being will loosen up, release and let go and when he slides inside of you, your pussy will be relaxed.

3) Another great move is to become very, very oral and hands-on with your man's cock before intercourse---but refrain from making him cum. The more time that you spend sucking, licking, kissing and playing with his cock with your lips, tongue, mouth and hands, the less time and stimulation he will need inside of you to reach his climax.

~Cock Complexities~

Yes, it does really happen to every man at some point in his life... a Loss-of-an-Erection, a Can't-Get-It-Up, even a depressing Loss-of-Desire to have sex.

So, take the initiative and bone-up on the following information and you'll know how to deal when and/or if, your man's cock unexpectedly won't erect:

Corralling ED:

Erectile Dysfunction is the applied medical term for when a man cannot get hard in any way for sex, or stay hard long enough to finish having sex. ED is a result of decreased blood flow to a man's cock, and 50% of all men have had trouble getting an erection because of ED at some stage in their lives. ED is a very normal occurrence that can easily be diagnosed and corralled. In this narrative, I describe the term Erectile Dysfunction as a Physical problem, and I use the label *Impotence* when the problem is clearly a *Psychological* one.

Here is the difference between the two:

Origin of Erectile Dysfunction:	Foundation for Impotence:
Brain injury	Alcohol
Diabetes	Depression
Hypertension	Drugs
Liver/Kidney Failure	Emotional Anxiety
Multiple Sclerosis	Relationship Troubles
Parkinson's Disease	Smoking
Prostate Problems	Stress from any source
Spinal Cord injury	
Stroke	
Other Health problems	

Impeding Physical Erectile Dysfunction:

Most men with a *Physical* Erectile Dysfunction can take PDE5 Inhibitors (oral ED medication) such as Viagra, Cialis and Levitra, when prescribed by a doctor who knows a man's medical history. While each of these ED drugs work differently, they all accomplish the same main goal: getting blood to flow through a man's cock so that he can have an erection with completion to a satisfying orgasm. Millions of men with Diabetes to Spinal Cord injuries have experienced renewed sexual activity with PDE5 Inhibitors, so this type of solution will definitely work for a healthier man.

Terminating *Psychological* Impotency

When a man has problems with Impotency, which I've termed *Psychological ED* for this work, his cock will get hard and he will have full erections during REM (deep) sleep. That Old Wives tale about stamping a man's cock to accurately determine if a man's erection problem is *Physical or Psychological*, is accurate: if you take a about 5-7 connected-perforated stamps, then lick and stick the stamps overlapping the last stamp to the first stamp, either to the base or under the circumcised rim of the head of his flaccid cock. If the stamps break or split apart while he's sleeping, this means blood was able to flow to his cock and swell his cock to an erection, producing an erection while his brain was at relaxation and rest.*

Psychological Impotency may be terminated if a man stops drinking, smoking and using recreational drugs in excess; when he finds positive ways to alleviate stress and anxiety; or as soon as he talks with someone about his depression or attends positive Couple's Therapy with his mate to expel difficulties in the romantic relationship.

Preventing PE:

Premature Ejaculation is what happens when he cums right *before*, at the *moment of*, or right *after* penetration of your pussy. Many of the men who are diagnosed with PE (one-third of them!) are as young as 25. In all, 33% of sexually active men experience PE. PE is often the first indicator that a man will develop ED.

Being unable to control how quickly he cums is primarily the consequence of all those 'quickies' he accomplished with the multiple girls he dated while fucking in his high school and college hookup years. Going from Fast-Food Fucking to Gourmet Sex with you is not something that his cock will have the capability to handle On Notice; therefore, his cock needs to be re-programmed to take sex into long-term satisfying intensity and away from the immediate short-term level he has been on all of his sex life. Premature Ejaculation is something that can naturally be conquered if he is willing to do something about it and if you are enthusiastic about assisting him.

Cock Re-Training Exercises:

Step One: Have him sit in a straight chair and dry-masturbate in front of you. This means no lubricant of any kind; not even his wet hand! Watch how he strokes his cock and pay particular attention to his face as he's about to cum. This is extremely important, because you can use his about-to-cum expression as your stop sign when you are stimulating him.

Step Two: The next day, or later that same day if he's willing, ask him to dry-masturbate for you again. Advise him that as soon as he feels like he is about to cum, to *immediately* stop stroking his cock and to release his cock from the grip of his hand. He may be unable to immediately stop stroking his cock the first few times he attempts this exercise, but practice will teach him to stop stroking as soon as he feels like he's about to cum. When he releases his cock from the grip of his hand, the loss-of-pressure and friction will usually stop him from achieving orgasm. After a moment of his sitting motionless, he'll need to repeat the above: stroking and stopping, stroking and stopping, stroking and stopping, until he builds-up cum tension and withholding longevity in his cock. When he builds-up to *fifteen minutes* without cuming, you can take him into your own hands.

Step Three: Once you've taken control of his cock, you can really make him the Master of Sex. Put on some slow music, like lazy Jazz or blues music without lyrics. Lay him flat on your bed and use a special topical-lotion on his cock just for this purpose... a product such as Maxoderm, which you can find online at www.maxoderm.biz/max_system. html. This is a natural herb product that will help your man hold a sturdier and harder erection. After you've massaged his cock with the lotion, slowly begin to stroke him in the same method that he uses when he masturbates. Watch his face so that you'll see his expression, when he is about to cum. When you see that expression, stop stoking his cock and release it from your grip. Keep doing this until he has experienced *twenty-five minutes* of your hands without an orgasm. What you are doing is relaxing him and setting-him-up for vaginal penetration: you're getting his cock used to your hand and your direction, so that he will feel comfortable and have less anxiety for the next move, which is cock-diving into your pussy.

Now that he's ready for vaginal penetration, your first few times having intercourse while combating PE, is to do It: 1) Missionary-Style or 2) with you On Top.

Vaginal Intercourse should begin as follows:

A) Ask him to move his cock in circular motions, rather than a thrusting in and out motion.

B) Advise him that when he feels he is about to cum, to stop and lay still or to pull out of you immediately.

C) Each time he stops moving, lays still and pulls out of you, gently massage his shoulders and butt and run your fingers down his lower back, because it will keep him relaxed and focused.

D) Even if he's inside you for five minutes before cuming, that is a huge accomplishment... and after a time of repetition, your man's cock will be re-programmed to the enjoyment of long-lasting intercourse.

Premature Ejaculation is not something that can be quickly overcome. It may take weeks or months to re-program his cock. However long it takes, do not give up and do not become frustrated with him and watch the words that come out of your mouth: PE *is not his fault* and he should not be emotionally punished by you because of it.

Andropause:

All those jokes that you may have made about a man having his period without bleeding or going through man-o-pause, have turned out to be closer to the truth than to a joke. Andropause is the applied medical term for when a man's sex drive has slowly diminished or he has completely lost all desire for sex because of a decline in his hormones, primarily testosterone, DHEA, thyroid hormone, and growth hormone. Stress, poor lifestyle, lack-of exercise, and improper diet also help contribute to Andropause.

Andropause can affect men as early as age twenty-five, because production of testosterone begins to drop off due to reduced production of luteinizing hormone in the pituitary gland. This can start in his mid-to-late twenties and it is a condition that has physical symptoms. Men who begin to experience Andropause are zapped of energy, have morose mood-swings, a decline in mental quickness and sharpness, diminished sexual function and/or sensitivity and decreased sex drive.

The best thing you can do is do research about Andropause online, and then gently get your man to go see his doctor if you suspect he's got it. What's good for him is that unlike Menopause in women, Andropause in men can be cured with hormones and a better, healthier lifestyle. Get your man checked-out if you think this could be happening to him.

~Top Cock Erectors~

You can make your man, and his Personal Playmate happy, by bringing great Cock Erection toys into the bedroom.

Here are some of the BEST cock-rings manufactured for his (and your) pleasure... and you can purchase these cock-rings and many more lovely, brilliant and inventive cock toys at www.babeland.com. What's so spectacular about this website is that it was created for women, by women, and they feature sex-toy advice on everything... even how to properly use a cock-ring!

 Teardrop Cock Ring... this is heavy and shaped like a large, hollow teardrop; he can wear this chrome cock ring in several ways. He can slide his cock or balls through the ring and point the teardrop backwards so it stimulates his perineum (anal area) during masturbation or when you are fucking him. He can put the ring between his testicles and the base of his cock, with the teardrop pointing forwards, so that the ring will gently cup his balls while the rounded tip will rub against your clit during intercourse. Because it's made of solid metal, the weight adds a bit of ball-stretching to the Teardrop's other talents. This is not a cock ring for beginners, and if you want great information on how to use Cock Rings, visit www.babeland.com and read their Advice on Cock Rings.

Blue Dolphin... this is a wireless, soft, pliable erection arouser has two powerful bullets to arouse you and keep him Hard both you and him. It provides fabulous cordless vibration for both partners. The ring stretches and easily fits over his cock and will vibrate against his testicles and keep his cock stimulated for Hardness. www.babeland.com

Black Nubble... this one inch black pliable rubber ring will stretch up to four times its size as you pull it over his cock and behind his testicles for the classic squeeze that helps men enjoy a Hard erection. The ring's knobble shapes create a pleasant stimulation on your vestibule. www.babeland.com

Orbit Ring Vibe... this is made of soft, stretchy jelly rubber, and goes over his cock, shaft or balls. This vibrating cock-ring can be set to the variable speed of his and/or your liking. Turn the vibrator downward for vibration on his testicles or turn it upward during sex with you, to provide an intense and consistent stimulation during vaginal penetration. www.babeland.com

Erector Set... this is an extra stretchy, vibrating jelly rubber cock-ring, has sensation-spiking ribs and nubs. The Sterling Vibe is waterproof, and will vibrate against his balls during sex, to keep him hard in the water or on land. www.babeland.com

~Wrapping Him Up~

As a sex expert, what I love most about doing research is finding the perfect spot where it all comes together. My great friend, Adam Glickman, is the owner/CEO and founder of the Condomania stores on both coasts, as well as the online internet store, www.condomania.com. Not only does this site entertain on sex and educate about sex, but it sells the only TheyFit condoms for the world's first size-to-fit condom line in 94 custom-to-fit sizes. Adam says: "The preliminary results from an extensive study conducted by The Kinsey Institute and Indiana University comparing TheyFit Sized-to-Fit condoms to standard condoms indicate that TheyFit condoms reduce breakage rates by 100% for vaginal intercourse and 400% for anal intercourse. In addition, the vast majority of the 1700 study participants rated TheyFit much higher than the standard condom for both feel and comfort."

You can easily find the mail-in print for the TheyFit condom at www.condomania.com, so you can measure his cock and then send-off for your own Fit-Kit. On the following pages, I've also featured the most reliable and safest condoms marketed. Pay close attention because all condoms are not alike and these are the condoms that the experts at www.condomania.com recommended!

Introducing They-Fit, the world's first sized-to-fit condom line in 55 custom fit sizes for maximum pleasure & safety.

CONDOMania® FIT KIT™

To find your ideal condom, follow the instructions below to measure your Johnson and identify your custom size.

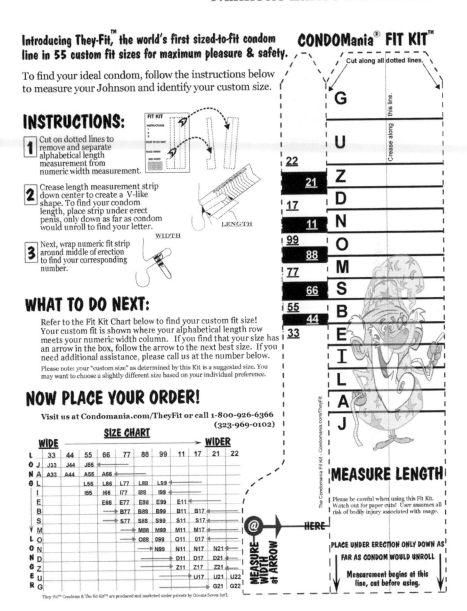

INSTRUCTIONS:

1 Cut on dotted lines to remove and separate alphabetical length measurement from numeric width measurement.

2 Crease length measurement strip down center to create a V-like shape. To find your condom length, place strip under erect penis, only down as far as condom would unroll to find your letter.

3 Next, wrap numeric fit strip around middle of erection to find your corresponding number.

WHAT TO DO NEXT:

Refer to the Fit Kit Chart below to find your custom fit size! Your custom fit is shown where your alphabetical length row meets your numeric width column. If you find that your size has an arrow in the box, follow the arrow to the next best size. If you need additional assistance, please call us at the number below.

Please note: your "custom size" as determined by this Kit is a suggested size. You may want to choose a slightly different size based on your individual preference.

NOW PLACE YOUR ORDER!

Visit us at Condomania.com/TheyFit or call 1-800-926-6366 (323-969-0102)

SIZE CHART

WIDE ———————→ WIDER

	33	44	55	66	77	88	99	11	17	21	22
J	J33	J44	J55								
A	A33	A44	A55	A66							
L			L55	L66	L77	L88	L99				
I			I55	I66	I77	I88	I99				
E				E66	E77	E88	E99	E11			
B					B77	B88	B99	B11	B17		
S					S77	S88	S99	S11	S17		
M						M88	M99	M11	M17		
O						O88	O99	O11	O17		
N							N99	N11	N17	N21	
D								D11	D17	D21	
Z								Z11	Z17	Z21	
U									U17	U21	U22
G										G21	G22

(Left margin: LONG / LONGER; bottom-right of chart: MEASURE WIDTH at ARROW — @ — HERE)

They-Fit™ Condoms & The Fit Kit™ are produced and marketed under patents by Oceans Seven Int'l.

MEASURE LENGTH

Please be careful when using this Fit Kit. Watch out for paper cuts! User assumes all risk of bodily injury associated with usage.

PLACE UNDER ERECTION ONLY DOWN AS FAR AS CONDOM WOULD UNROLL

Measurement begins at this line, cut before using.

Cut along all dotted lines. Crease along this line.

The Condomania Fit Kit · Condomania.com/TheyFit

Lifestyles Large Condoms have a unique flared tip for a more relaxed fit, perfect for the generously endowed gent. Lightly lubricated for easy-glide penetration, with durable latex for extra protection. www.condomania.com

Kimono MAXX Condoms provide greater comfort and coverage. The contour shape makes MAXX easy to put on, and the silky, natural latex makes sex more enjoyable. www.condomania.com

 Durex XXL Condoms are extra large for big time pleasure, with reservoir-end and fitted shape for easy-on and great feel. Nominal width: 54mm. www.condomania.com

 Lifestyles Snugger Fit Condoms are specially designed to hug his cock better, with Ultra-Sensitive condom with a unique, special shape and lubricated for a natural feeling with a reservoir tip for added comfort and safety. www.condomania.com.

 Performax by Durex is lubed on the outside for more thrusting and lubed on the inside with an exclusive Climax Control desensitizer. www.condomania.com

 Marathon Condoms offer lasting pleasure two ways: lubed on the outside for smoother thrusting and the inside has Climax Control desensitizer. www.condomania.com

Lifestyles Warming Pleasure is a totally new kind of condom! These comfortable condoms are coated with a warming lubricant that's activated by his natural body moisture. You'll both feel gentle sensations of warmth! www.condomania.com

Fe-Male is a great new condom that is pre-lubricated with *four times* the usual amount of lubricant! Aloe has also been added for increased comfort and s-m-o-o-t-h-e-r sex! www.condomania.com

Kimono Micro Thin Plus is 38% thinner than regular condoms, and offers maximum transparency, sensitivity, and feeling, featuring a reservoir end. This is a truly superior condom that is manufactured in Japan. www.condomania.com

Beyond Seven condoms are made of Sheerlon, an advanced material so strong and durable, these are *the* super thin condom! Its diversity can be seen and felt. It is textured with ribs and dots and lightly lubricated. www.condomania.com

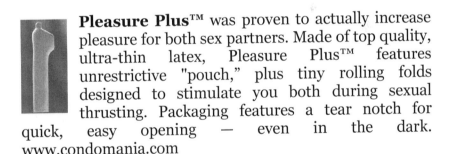

Pleasure Plus™ was proven to actually increase pleasure for both sex partners. Made of top quality, ultra-thin latex, Pleasure Plus™ features unrestrictive "pouch," plus tiny rolling folds designed to stimulate you both during sexual thrusting. Packaging features a tear notch for quick, easy opening — even in the dark. www.condomania.com

Inspiral there's nothing like it! The loose-fitting tip swirls around the penis head producing crazy friction for both partners! This condom makes it easier for women achieve orgasms easier and sooner during intercourse! www.condomania.com

Trojan Twisted Pleasure Condoms are the most wild and innovative condom to-date from America's most trusted condom manufacturer. In the tradition of the exotic-shaped Pleasure Plus and InSpiral, Trojan's unique "twist" at the closed end is designed to stimulate both partners in their most sensitive areas. The loose, extreme shape produces an exciting dynamic action that stimulates nerve ending and heightens sensitivity. www.condomania.com

Trojan Naturalamb Condoms made from a natural pouch in the lambs' intestines, provide a popular alternative to latex. Men prefer natural skin condoms due to the enhanced sensitivity and extraordinary durability of the natural skin. Others enjoy the exceptionally large width of natural skin condoms. *Due to the size of the pores in natural skin condoms, they are not recommended for the prevention of disease.* Trojan Naturalamb is only natural skin condom currently on the market. www.condomania.com

Trojan Supra Condoms were introduced after a decade of research and development and are only one of two polyurethane condoms widely available. The U.S. Trojan Supra is made from a highly advanced formula called Microsheer that is ultra-thin, soft, and hypoallergenic and boasts no taste or smell. Trojan Supra can be used with oil based lubricants and is heat conductive, warming to body temperature. Perhaps most incredibly, Trojan Supra is almost invisible. In fact it is so clear we had to use a plant in the picture so you could see the darn thing! www.condomania.com

ONE Condom Studded have unique circular packaging, each featuring different thematic designs that are continually introduced. Besides an edgy modern appearance, ONE Condoms also provide unbeatable quality, comfort and reliability. Each and every ONE is made with extra-comfortable, premium latex. The raised texture of 576 studs enhances performance by awakening intense sensations. www.condomania.com

 Durex Avanti Polyurethane Condoms are about half as thin as most latex condoms and are non-porous and non-permeable to all viruses, including HIV. Heat conductive (warms to body temperature) and safe to use with oil based lubricants, as well as Hypoallergenic (great for anyone allergic to latex). www.condomania.com

~Recommended Cock Reading~

 Dick: A User's Guide by Drs. Michele Moore and Caroline de Costa is an information-packed handbook to the penis, covering everything from physiology and hygiene, to sex and masturbation. Included, is a clever resource manual and an entertaining directory of slang terms for The Cock.

 DICK: A Guide to the Penis for Men and Women by Drs. Michele Moore and Caroline de Costa is lovely, lovely, lovely! After reading this book, the first thing you will want to do when you see him, is go on an exploratory expedition of his cock!

The Penis Book by Joseph Cohen commemorates the male member like nothing else before. You will learn, laugh, love what you've read and be thoroughly titillated. 'The Penis Book' has something for every woman who reads it.

Sex, the Heart and Erectile Dysfunction by Graham Jackson is a very informative book that supplies the reader with straightforward course of action on the pharmacological, social and sexual benefits of correct dosing in various types of patient groups.

~Recommended PE Websites~

www.afraidtoask.com
www.bostonmedicalgroup.com/premature-ejaculation
www.emedicine.com
www. health-nexus.com/premature_ejaculation11. htm
www.malehealthcenter.com
www.stayerect.com

Recommended ED and Impotency Websites:

www.familydoctor.org
www.erecthard.com
www.erectile-dysfunction-impotence.org
www.impotent.com
www.emedicinehealth.com
www.impotence.org
www.erectile-dysfunction-advisor.com
www.menshealth.com
www.ehealthmd.com
www.erectile-dysfunction-treatment.org
www.malehealthcenter.com

~Recommended Info about His Cock Websites~

www.condomania.com
www.ratemycock.com
www.my-penis.org
www.penis-website.com/penis. html
www.penishealth.com
www.the-penis.com

A *Phallophile* is a person who is obsessed with penises (which is what I hope you'll be after reading this book!). A man named Sigurdur Hjartarson, who resides in Reykjavik, Iceland, has opened the World's only Cock museum, called the *Icelandic Phallological Museum*. I think that is lovely idea. If women can have the *Vagina Monologs*, then there should be a museum in honor of Man's Prized Possession: His Cock!

Love your man's cock!

thefuckingtruththefuckingtruththefuckingtruththefuckingtruththefu
ckingtruththefuckingtruththefuckingtruththefuckingtruththefucking
truththefuckingtruththefuckingtruththefuckingtruththefuckingtruth
thefuckingtruththefuckingtruththefuckingtruththefuckingtruththefu
ckingtruththefuckingtruththefuckingtruththefuckingtruththefucking
truththefuckingtruththefuckingtruththefuckingtruththefuckingtruth
thefuckingtruththefuckingtruththefuckingtruththefuckingtruththefu
ckingtruththefuckingtruththefuckingtruththefuckingtruththefucking
truththefuckingtruththefuckingtruththefuckingtruththefuckingtruth
thefuckingtruththefuckingtruththefuckingtruththefuckingtruththefu
ckingtruththefuckingtruththefuckingtruththefuckingtruththefucking

On: Fucking ~ The Truth

truththefuckingtruththefuckingtruththefuckingtruththefuckingtruth
thefuckingtruththefuckingtruththefuckingtruththefuckingtruththefu
ckingtruththefuckingtruththefuckingtruththefuckingtruththefucking
truththefuckingtruththefuckingtruththefuckingtruththefuckingtruth
thefuckingtruththefuckingtruththefuckingtruththefuckingtruththefu
ckingtruththefuckingtruththefuckingtruththefuckingtruththefucking
truththefuckingtruththefuckingtruththefuckingtruththefuckingtruth
thefuckingtruththefuckingtruththefuckingtruththefuckingtruththefu
ckingtruththefuckingtruththefuckingtruththefuckingtruththefucking
truththefuckingtruththefuckingtruththefuckingtruththefuckingtruth
thefuckingtruththefuckingtruththefuckingtruththefuckingtruththefu
ckingtruththefuckingtruththefuckingtruththefuckingtruththefucking
truththefuckingtruththefuckingtruththefuckingtruththefuckingtruth
thefuckingtruththefuckingtruththefuckingtruththefuckingtruththefu
ckingtruththefuckingtruththefuckingtruththefuckingtruththefucking
truththefuckingtruththefuckingtruththefuckingtruththefuckingtruth
thefuckingtruththefuckingtruththefuckingtruththefuckingtruththefu
ckingtruththefuckingtruththefuckingtruththefuckingtruththefucking
truththefuckingtruththefuckingtruththefuckingtruththefuckingtruth
thefuckingtruththefuckingtruththefuckingtruththefuckingtruththefu
ckingtruththefuckingtruththefuckingtruththefuckingtruththefucking
truththefuckingtruththefuckingtruththefuckingtruththefuckingtruth
thefuckingtruththefuckingtruththefuckingtruththefuckingtruththefu
ckingtruththefuckingtruththefuckingtruththefuckingtruththefucking
truththefuckingtruththefuckingtruththefuckingtruththefuckingtruth
thefuckingtruththefuckingtruththefuckingtruththefuckingtruththefu
ckingtruththefuckingtruththefuckingtruththefuckingtruththefucking
truththefuckingtruththefuckingtruththefuckingtruththefuckingtruth
thefuckingtruththefuckingtruththefuckingtruththefuckingtruththefu
ckingtruththefuckingtruththefuckingtruththefuckingtruththefucking

IV. On: Fucking ~ The Truth

There are two kinds of women: those who want power in the world and those who want power in bed.

~~~Jacqueline Kennedy Onassis

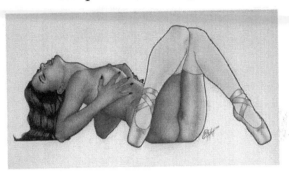

Artist Kathryn Hitt of the San Francisco Bay Area
Artwork featured at: www.gradiva.com

Naughty Girls.
Nasty Girls.
Sluts.

Women who blatantly flaunt their sexuality, freely offer their favors, fuck with fearless abandon, generously sprawl their naked bodies for the lusty eye of the camera. Ejaculated Madonnaism at its nipple-coned peak; trashy women who apparently have no Self-Respect.

All of your life you've been programmed to believe:

... that the woman who can fuck any man or even her own man, just for fun and without Emotional Sentiment...

... that the woman who ardently spreads her legs for the simple thrall of lustful pleasure...

... that the woman who savors the cum that splashes onto her face and drips off her breasts while she yearns for the musky smell of a man's body saturated in her skin...

... that the woman whose first reflection and hungering thought after sex is not: *"Does he still love me?"* but rather, *"I wonder if McDonald's is still open!"*...

... that the woman who pollens her sexuality to a wide world of men with a giggle and a bounce...

... That woman cannot look in the mirror possibly like whom she sees or who she is.

Well, here is the confident **Truth about Fucking**.

About That woman.

That is the woman who lets go for a wild, lustful ride on a naked buck of a man and willingly and conscience-freely gratifies her own carnal desires and fantasies as well as his, has more love and Self-Respect wrapped up in her semen-soiled g-string than the woman who denies her sensual aches and sexual desires of uninhibited lust for the inhibited sake and fear of how society will label her behavior has in her whole body.

Any woman who knows how to enjoy a fuck and relishes the sport of a fuck, does not fuck because it is her man's request, plea, demand, bidding or right. Neither does she fuck for reinforcement of her value or for the need of any man's stamp-of-approval, nor, in fact, does she search for true love through the vise of any sexual thrall... because whether or not *that* woman is in a committed relationship or if she is completely unattached, *that* woman understands, acknowledges and appreciates that sometimes *A Fuck Is Just A Fuck.*

Any woman who does and can, without rhyme or guilt, demand or commitment, hope or need... willingly and freely fuck a man with such an aching and delicious abandon *completely respects herself.*

Artist CJGA
artwork is Featured at: www.eroticalee.com

suckhiscocksuckhiscocksuckhiscocksuckhiscocksuckhiscocksuckhiscoc
ksuckhiscocksuckhiscocksuckhiscocksuckhiscocksuckhiscocksuckhisco
cksuckhiscocksuckhiscocksuckhiscocksuckhiscocksuckhiscocksuckhisc
ocksuckhiscocksuckhiscocksuckhiscocksuckhiscocksuckhiscocksuckhis
cocksuckhiscocksuckhiscocksuckhiscocksuckhiscocksuckhiscocksuckhi
scocksuckhiscocksuckhiscocksuckhiscocksuckhiscocksuckhiscocksuckh
iscocksuckhiscocksuckhiscocksuckhiscocksuckhiscocksuckhiscocksuck
hiscocksuckhiscocksuckhiscocksuckhiscocksuckhiscocksuckhiscocksuc
khiscocksuckhiscocksuckhiscocksuckhiscocksuckhiscocksuckhiscocksu
ckhiscocksuckhiscocksuckhiscocksuckhiscocksuckhiscocksuckhiscocks
uckhiscocksuckhiscocksuckhiscocksuckhiscocksuckhiscocksuckhiscock
suckhiscocksuckhiscocksuckhiscocksuckhiscocksuckhiscocksuckhiscoc
ksuckhiscocksuckhiscocksuckhiscocksuckhiscocksuckhiscocksuckhisco
cksuckhiscocksuckhiscocksuckhiscocksuckhiscocksuckhiscocksuckhisc
ocksuckhiscocksuckhiscocksuckhiscocksuckhiscocksuckhiscocksuckhis

Nuclear Head

cocksuckhiscocksuckhiscocksuckhiscocksuckhiscocksuckhiscocksuckhi
scocksuckhiscocksuckhiscocksuckhiscocksuckhiscocksuckhiscocksuckh
iscocksuckhiscocksuckhiscocksuckhiscocksuckhiscocksuckhiscocksuck
hiscocksuckhiscocksuckhiscocksuckhiscocksuckhiscocksuckhiscocksuc
khiscocksuckhiscocksuckhiscocksuckhiscocksuckhiscocksuckhiscocksu
ckhiscockSuckhiscocksuckhiscocksuckhiscocksuckhiscocksuckhiscocks
uckhiscocksuckhiscocksuckhiscocksuckhiscocksuckhiscocksuckhiscock
suckhiscocksuckhiscocksuckhiscocksuckhiscocksuckhiscocksuckhiscoc
ksuckhiscocksuckhiscocksuckhiscocksuckhiscocksuckhiscocksuckhisco
cksuckhiscocksuckhiscocksuckhiscocksuckhiscocksuckhiscocksuckhisc
ocksuckhiscocksuckhiscocksuckhiscocksuckhiscocksuckhiscocksuckhis
cocksuckhiscocksuckhiscocksuckhiscocksuckhiscocksuckhiscocksuckhi
scocksuckhiscocksuckhiscocksuckhiscocksuckhiscocksuckhiscocksuckh
iscocksuckhiscocksuckhiscocksuckhiscocksuckhiscocksuckhiscocksuck
hiscocksuckhiscocksuckhiscocksuckhiscocksuckhiscocksuckhiscocksuc
khiscocksuckhiscocksuckhiscocksuckhiscocksuckhiscocksuckhiscocksu
ckhiscocksuckhiscocksuckhiscocksuckhiscocksuckhiscocksuckhiscocks
uckhiscocksuckhiscocksuckhiscocksuckhiscocksuckhiscocksuckhiscock
suckhiscocksuckhiscocksuckhiscocksuckhiscocksuckhiscocksuckhiscoc
ksuckhiscocksuckhiscocksuckhiscocksuckhiscocksuckhiscocksuckhisco
cksuckhiscocksuckhiscocksuckhiscocksuckhiscocksuckhiscocksuckhisc
ocksuckhiscocksuckhiscocksuckhiscocksuckhiscocksuckhiscocksuckhis
cocksuckhiscocksuckhiscocksuckhiscocksuckhiscocksuckhiscocksuckhi
scocksuckhiscocksuckhiscocksuckhiscocksuckhiscocksuckhiscocksuckh
iscocksuckhiscocksuckhiscocksuckhiscocksuckhiscocksuckhiscocksuck
hiscocksuckhiscocksuckhiscocksuckhiscocksuckhiscocksuckhiscocksuc
khiscocksuckhiscocksuckhiscocksuckhiscocksuckhiscocksuckhiscocksu
ckhiscocksuckhiscocksuckhiscocksuckhiscocksuckhiscocksuckhiscocks
uckhiscocksuckhiscocksuckhiscocksuckhiscocksuckhiscocksuckhiscock
suckhiscocksuckhiscocksuckhiscocksuckhiscocksuckhiscocksuckhiscoc
ksuckhiscocksuckhiscocksuckhiscocksuckhiscocksuckhiscocksuckhisco
cksuckhiscocksuckhiscocksuckhiscocksuckhiscocksuckhiscocksuckhisc
ocksuckhiscocksuckhiscocksuckhiscocksuckhiscocksuckhiscocksuckhis
cocksuckhiscocksuckhiscocksuckhiscocksuckhiscocksuckhiscocksuckhi
scocksuckhiscocksuckhiscocksuckhiscocksuckhiscocksuckhiscocksuckh
iscocksuckhiscocksuckhiscocksuckhiscocksuckhiscocksuckhiscocksuck
hiscocksuckhiscocksuckhiscocksuckhiscocksuckhiscocksuckhiscocksuc
khiscocksuckhiscocksuckhiscocksuckhiscocksuckhiscocksuckhiscocksu
ckhiscocksuckhiscocksuckhiscocksuckhiscocksuckhiscocksuckhiscocks
uckhiscocksuckhiscocksuckhiscocksuckhiscocksuckhiscocksuckhiscock
suckhiscocksuckhiscocksuckhiscocksuckhiscocksuckhiscocksuckhiscoc

V. Nuclear Head

*...your man's Cum is definitely the great elixir;
a soothing balm for your soul... Bon Appetit.*

~~~Samantha, California
(quote taken from www.dontspitswallow.com)

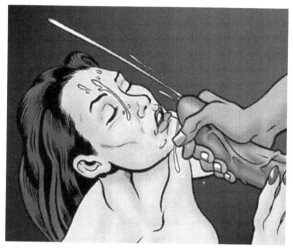

Artist "EL STABO" of New York City
Artwork featured at: www.gradiva.com

Every man yearns for a woman that can really suck cock.
And when your man visualizes a great fuck, having his cock
sucked by you is at the top of his Sexual Wish List. Your
man's cock embodies 95% of his Ego, and the Number #1
unsurpassed way that you can prove to your man that you
adore him, *is when you worship his cock.*

Therefore: His Cock = His Ego.

Believe it.

I guarantee you that every man *needs* to have his cock
sucked... and I assure you that every man relishes, enjoys,
and dreams about having his cock sucked... and if you are
not sucking your man's cock than you'd better understand
this: if your man has an actual opportunity to dip his cock
into the mouth of any other woman who is willing to suck
it, *he will.* When doing research for this book, 97% of the
9,826 men that I talked to named oral sex neglect from

their woman as their number one complaint in their romantic relationship.

And here is where it really gets good...

Disregard all the nasty, wicked, naughty, pleasurable, rank or imaginative sex you've seen portrayed in porn flicks or in the movies or in the spicy XXX stories you may have read in publications such as *Penthouse Forum* or in *My Secret Life* magazines or written on the Internet... because there isn't one man in your county, rural area, city, suburb, town, metropolis or borough that is being fucked that good by his wife, girlfriend or lover. *Why else would Internet Porn be a trillion-dollar-a-year industry?!*

Think about it: if the guy next door were getting his cock gratifyingly sucked by his woman, how much oomph do you think he'd have to have to religiously slide-up to the computer monitor and view a hot Internet chick sucking-off some other lucky bastard?! What's worse, I've discovered that the majority of men who have the biggest number of sexual conquests have actually had less-satisfactory and much more disappointing and blasé sex, than men who have had fewer bed partners!

Trust me, nearly all *"experienced"* men are oblivious to the definition of exceptionally-gratifying sex... and very few men have ever had the pleasure or the privilege of experiencing a cremating orgasm that sends them into orbit... and most men do not realize how very, very little they either know about sex or how very, very little pleasure they have ever gotten from sex... until they fuck a woman who has the skill and the desire to s-l-o-w-l-y suck them into overdrive and down that road to Sexual Insanity.

~Exploring Your Man's Cock~

You can become an expert at knowing his cock as well as he does if you really take the time to explore, observe and 'get to know it', by touch and sight. Each man's cock is as different as every snowflake that falls from the sky, and how he needs it touched and sucked is as unique to him as is his personality.

While a man's cock may appear to be nothing more-than a solid, hairy muscle with dangling balls and a little cap - what a man's cock actually is, is the core component of his entire physical, mental and emotional existence. Once again: *A man's cock embodies 95% of his Ego, and the Number #1 unsurpassed way that you can prove to your man that you adore him, is when you worship his cock.*

Therefore: his cock = his ego.

Once you're on familiar terms with his cock and you've become skilled at how to touch him and suck him, *you're the one who owns It.*

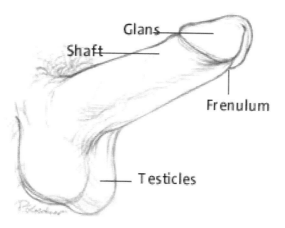

www.secretgardenpublishing.com

The V-shaped area on the base of his *glans* and his *frenulum* is one of the most vulnerable spots on his cock. His *perineum* (not shown) is that area right at the back of his *balls* (testicles), and is about halfway between his *scrotum* and his *anus*. His *perineum* will react to the pleasure of consistent and unrelenting pressure by your fingers, which will arouse him via his prostate area. That *dark blue ridge* (the urethral line) on his shaft was named by me as *The Nibble-n-March Track*, because if you nibble him there with your teeth or march your fingertips up and down that *dark blue ridge* and it will drive him feral! The most sensitive part of his cock is the *head* - aka his glans. If he is circumcised, bestow lots of mouthy attention to that raised ring around the *head* of his cock (the corona), as well as to his V-Spot. Remember his scrotum and his balls with a very sweet and delicate licking, kissing, sucking and kneading.

www.secretgardenpublishing.com

~Sweet Sucks~

There are all sorts of great techniques to sucking your man's cock... and if you love what you're doing for the desire and the gratification of him, then he will appreciate how you pleasure him just because you're willingly touching him and not because you've made it to the Blow Job Olympics. However, if you want to really spice-up your Head-Job routine with him, then you can mix-in one or all of the following to your lusty repertoire:

The Goddess Suck:

*Ask him to kneel on the bed or on the floor, with his hands palms down and his legs spread.

*Slide your body face-up between his legs, until your mouth is aligned with his dangling cock.

*Take his cock into your mouth and begin to suck him off. While you suck his cock, gently but firmly massage the tiny pink pucker of his asshole.

*When you can feel and hear that he's about to cum, glide his cock as deep into your throat as you can, then slide the finger you've been using to massage his ass, downward and smoothly into his tiny pink hole. As he cums, press down firmly on his prostate gland.

The Blindfold Blow:

*Take a silk or satin strip of cloth, and cover his eyes with it. Make sure that the knot is flat, so that he's comfortable when you lay him down against the pillows.

*Spread his legs wide and lube-up his cock.

*Ask him to fantasize that you are his favorite video or internet porn star or movie star that is sucking him off.

*Lick, kiss, nibble and suck him everywhere on his nether region until he cums.

The Kitty Lick:

*Cats'-cradle his cock tightly with your hands while your mouth slides up-and-down all over his shaft.

*With your teeth, give sharp, tiny nips along the bluish vein that runs underneath his cock to the glands and frenulum up-and-down ~named by me as *The Nibble-n-March Track*. Repeat this twenty times.

*After the twentieth time, slide your lips up and abruptly suction the head of his cock into your lips as hard has you can, while you quickly stroke his cock with your interlaced hands until he cums.

The Six String-Band:

*Take six medium, small or large cloth-covered hair bands (what you use depends on the width of his cock), and starting at the base of his well-lubed cock, slide on the hair bands until each one is strung 1-6 from the base of his cock to the head of his cock.

*With your teeth, tongue and lips *only*, remove each one of those six strings. All the sucking, pressure and determination on your part just to remove the six bands from around his cock may cause him to cum quicker than you think!

The SOS Suck:

*Slide your mouth all the way down the shaft of his cock to the base.

*Suck extraordinarily and intensely-hard while moving your mouth back up the shaft of his cock to the head of his cock, in a *constant and consistent* movement until he cums.

The ABC's of Head:

*A: suck the head of his cock with your lips.

*B: stroke the shaft of his cock with one hand.

*C: massage his balls with the palm and fingers from your other hand. *An ABC is doing this* all *at the same time.*

The Classic Suck:

*Lie on your back, flat on the bed or the floor.

*Tell him to straddle you until his knees are almost underneath your underarms and against the sides of your breasts. Ask him if he wants to cum in your mouth, in your face or on your breasts.

*Direct him to gently slide his hard cock into your mouth. Breathe in through your nose and caress his balls and/or run your hands between his thighs and all over his ass, as his cock moves inside your mouth.

*Keep the sucking rhythm until he cums.

~Guidelines for Sucking an Uncircumcised Penis~

An uncircumcised cock is easy to identify because the head of his cock will resemble a turtle, and when he's soft, his cock-head will recoil back into the alcove of that excess of skin. Even when he is hard, some of his uncircumcised skin might still cover-up most of the head of his cock.

Because an uncircumcised cock is far more sensitive than a circumcised cock, you need to make sure that you take extra precautions when you give him Head. Here are a few guidelines to ensuring his pleasure:

1) Lubricating his uncircumcised cock is very important, because the foreskin is very sensitive, and without good lubrication the friction of your mouth and hands can irritate and even cause tearing of the thin-skinned head of his cock. Therefore: *lubricate.*

As you begin, tenderly slide back the foreskin at the head of his cock and zealously lick with your tongue while you smoothly and evenly stroke the shaft with your fingertips just under the head of his cock to his balls. You can move the foreskin back by putting your taunt wet lips at the tip of his cock and sliding your mouth down his shaft, and you can apply appropriate pressure by asking him how he likes it, wants it and needs it.

3) Hold his cock at the base and after using slow mouth sucks and hand strokes, move your mouth from the head of his cock to the base so that you can caress his whole cock in your mouth. Then, using your tongue in circles around the head of his cock, suck him hard with your lips until he's ready to cum.

~The Genius of Deep Throating his Cock~

When his cock slides down your throat past your gag reflex, that it is "Deep Throating."

The oral cavity of your throat is only four-to-five inches deep and the average size cock is about six-inches long, so the biggest obstacle in your taking his entire cock down, is the fact that there is a bend of almost 90 degrees behind your tongue that leads down into your throat... and that's a whole lot to swallow... especially if his cock is longer than six-inches and is thick-round as well!

With a lot of practice, you *will* be able to take his cock deeper and deeper into your throat for longer periods of time, and you will become a pro at Deep Throating; even if he is 8-inches or more. However... you have to *religiously* practice or you'll never get be able to master his cock via Deep Throating.

~Helpful Tips When Deep Throating~

*Never Deep Throat his cock when your tummy is full, for instance, after you've had a heavy meal. Likewise, don't do it when you're drunk, because if you accidentally gag it will cause you to vomit, which is totally unsexy!

*You can build up your gag-reflex for excellent Deep Throating, *only* by exercise and practice. If you'll just imagine that you're studying for an exam where you have to get an A+ to pass, then you're sure to strengthen your gag-reflex in no time at all and your throat will flex and comfortably stretch to the size of his cock.

*Spray Chloraseptic into the back of your throat to numb it before you Deep Throat his cock. This will anesthetize the back of your throat, and that is a good thing.

*Gradually work-up to Deep Throating so that you will be able to overcome the involuntary reflex to gag. You can do this by practicing on him or on a dildo or vibrator.

*When first beginning to Deep Throat, position your body so that your mouth and throat are almost in a straight line, and lie flat on the bed so that your head is near the edge of the bed, tipped back sharply. This will give his cock better slide and your throat more leverage.

*Ask him to slowly slide the tip of his cock into your throat, and to hold his cock with one of his hands until you find the most comfortable way to proceed.

*Slowly take his cock as far back into your mouth and throat as you are able; about ½-an-inch-at-a-time~as you breath-in through your nose, while you swallow his cock.

*Your throat must be *completely relaxed* as he is thrusting his cock deeply down into your throat, so that when he cums, he can ejaculate straight-down past your gag-reflex, into your stomach.

~Practicing to Cum-Swallowing Perfection~
When you swallow his cum, it isn't just an ego-boost for him; it tells him that you adore him, love him, and worship him.

You can vary swallowing his cum by: giving him a Cum-Shot - having him cum in your face or on your breasts, your belly, your buttocks, your back, or in your hair. However, if you learn the skill of swallowing his cum, he'll adore you for it. Swallowing really does makes you a Keeper in his eyes.

Practicing to 'Big Gulp' Perfection:

 The only way to effectively achieve swallowing your man's load of cum when you give him Head, is by going as realistic as possible by purchasing an *Ejaculating Cock-Shaped Dildo* or an *Ejaculating Cock-Shaped Vibrator*. You can find many different types for purchase at your local adult 'toy' store or from any of the online places that I've listed in *'Erotic Accessories.'* *Ejaculating Cock-Shaped Dildos* and *Ejaculating Cock-Shaped Vibrators* each have a reservoir for 'cum-like' liquids and a hand-pump to spurt the liquid out of the cock-head. Most dildos and vibrators are usually bigger-than the average male cock... so don't lose your nerve if you have trouble accommodating it in your mouth. Just take it real slow and not only will you teach yourself to swallow his cum, but you'll also teach yourself how to Deep Throat his cock.

After you've purchase either an *Ejaculating Cock-Shaped Dildo* or *Ejaculating Cock-Shaped Vibrator*, and you've chosen which cum-substitute substance you want to fill it with, you're ready to go.

Once you've gotten your *Ejaculating Cock-Shaped Dildo* or *Ejaculating Cock-Shaped Vibrator* loaded, move it around and get relaxed with it in your mouth. Sliding it to the back of your throat and practicing with it to overcome your gag reflex. After several practices, take hold of the hand-pump and when you're ready, pump it with a quick squeeze and the cum-substitute will saturate your mouth. Quickly swallow if you can. If you've practiced enough and gotten the *Ejaculating Cock-Shaped Dildo* or *Ejaculating Cock-Shaped Vibrator* past your gag reflex so that the cum-substitute shoots down your throat, than you're ready to try swallowing in various positions like: A).on your side, B).laying on your back, C).leaning above the dildo/vibrator-cock as if your man were on his back or sitting up, and D). with your head flung-back and hanging-over the side of the bed. You should also experiment positioning your mouth in a different way for swallowing his cum, and see how it feels in the back of your throat versus your mouth. Compare multiple swallowing with saving it all in your mouth for one gulp.

To become a pro at swallowing your man's cum and Deep-Throating his cock, ask a friend to help you practice by moving the *Ejaculating Cock-Shaped Dildo* or *Ejaculating Cock-Shaped Vibrator* for you, fucking your mouth with it and spurting the cum-substitute without any advanced warning - this will emulate exactly what will happen when his shoots his cum into your mouth... and you'll need the rehearsal!

Special Recipes for 'Cum' Sauce:

If you want to become his Super Sucking Vixen by swallowing his cum, you'll first need to whip-up a batch of something with the consistency of his cum, and practice, practice, practice. There are several various substances you can use to create a semen-like stand-in:

1) Plain yogurt is the easiest and most palatable. Whip the plain yogurt with a fork until fully blended, and let the plain yogurt stand out at room temperature for twenty minutes for the perfect cum-like consistency. Add 1/4 tsp. salt per 1/2 cup of yogurt.

2) Tapioca pudding (though a little chunky) has a more accurate texture. If you can make it from scratch with less sugar and no vanilla flavoring, it's ideal. Add 1/4 tsp. salt per 1/2 cup pudding.

3) Canned condensed milk also works. Mix in an extra pinch of salt to duplicate his cum's salty flavor.

4) For the most-accurate texture, mix a lightly beaten egg white and two teaspoons full of hot water to get the right consistency.

For the best tips on swallowing your man's cum, please visit the website: www.dontspitswallow.com.

~Goddess of Head Tips~

*Tenderly suck his cock after he has orgasmed, and he begins to become softer. This is a very intimate act, and it will put him sweetly to sleep.

*Whenever you are in his line-of-vision, resolve to keep direct eye contact with him. Your eyes are the window to your soul and if you love sucking your man's cock, your eyes will tell him more than your words ever will.

*Your man is very visual. Mix it up a bit with sexy red panties or red thigh-highs, red painted nails and red lipstick. Then wrap your painted nails around his cock and slide the head of his cock into your painted red lips.

*Stroke his sacrum with soft, featherlike strokes to trigger the nerve endings from his lower spine to his neck.

*Before you suck him, ask your man if he wants you to swallow his cum or if he wants to do a cum-shot on your face, breasts, back or ass.

*Cock Cool-Downs:*dip his cock in Champagne or any carbonated beverage - the bubbles will make his cock tingle before you suck him off.* *take an ice cube and run it up-n-down his cock from Head to Base, and rub it around his balls.* *put a Listerine Breath Strip on your tongue then slide his cock into your mouth.* *swish liqueur Crème de Menthe in your mouth then slide his cock into the coolness.* *dunk his cock in a minty mouthwash, and then suck it off.* *place one of Hall's strong mentholated cough drops or a zesty Altoid breath mint inside your mouth and against one of your cheeks, then give him Head.*

*Soak his cock and balls in lubrication and drape your hair around the base of his cock as you suck the Head... then take a handful of your hair and smoothly begin to stroke the base his cock with your hair as you suck his cock-head into your lips.

*Hold one of his hands with your free hand, and make love to him with your eyes as you suck his cock.

*Stroke his cock with a satin or silk piece of material while you suckle on the head of his cock. When he's ready to cum, let him cum into the cloth.

*Acquire a 'Sixth Sense' for when he's about to cum by paying exclusive attention to how he moves, moans and breathes right before he cums.

*Design a hot blooded CD solely for when you give him Head, by downloading his favorite music off the Internet and burning it off your computer onto the CD.

*Purchase a kit of tooth-whitener that has the plastic upper and lower teeth covers for your front teeth. Next time you give him Head, secure the plastic teeth covers on your upper and lower teeth and then slide his cock between them... it will make him crazy, because it feels like your pussy is sucking his cock and he's getting two-for-one.

*Give his cock a head-rush... soak his cock in lubrication, then chew some Altoids Peppermint gum, and while the flavor is immediately present in your mouth blow your cold breath up and down and around his cock.

*If your hair is long enough, style it in two school-girl ponytails or braids. After he's cum in your mouth, throw your head back so that he can see your throat, and let his cum dribble slowly out of your mouth, down your throat onto your breasts.

*Slide your forefinger padded-side downward, inside his ass while sucking his cock, and when he's about to cum, push his cock into your throat, then press down on the cum-button deep inside his ass and his orgasm will be unfathomable.

*When you swallow his cum, leave the head of his cock inside your throat so that it constricts against it, giving him a throbbing, pussy-like sensation.

*Purchase a floor-length mirror and position it behind you. Put a soft-light in the bedroom lamp that will illuminate the mirror. Then, spread your legs in front of the mirror and give him Head, while he watches your ass move and how wet your pussy gets from sucking him off.

*Gently nibble-bite with your teeth around the head of his cock.

*Blindfold him and deprive him of the visual, so that he *feels* the Head Job more intensely.

*Eat Red Hots candy and swish the candy around in your mouth, then slide his cock between your lips and give him Red Hot-Head.

*After you've sucked him off, kiss and lick the inside of his thighs, his belly, his balls, his ass-cheeks... everywhere.

*When he's fucking your pussy, whisper in his ear and tell him when he's about to cum that you want to finish him off with your mouth. Then swallow all his cum while he watches.

*Wiggle and Jiggle your tongue inside the little opening in the tip of his cock.

*Moan and groan and whisper how yummy he is while you suck his cock.

*Move his cock to the side of your mouth for an easy Deep Throat move. Gently side-nibble on his cock with your teeth as he grinds inside your mouth.

*Look him in the eyes and give him sexy glances as you suck his cock~~~eye contact will always heighten his cock-sucking experience.

*Straddle one of his legs while you suck his cock and rub your wet pussy into his thigh until you come - it will drive him insane.

*Softly and slowly drag your teeth up and down the shaft of his cock.

~Good-Head Accessories~

 A&E Deep Throat Gel... take his cock all the way down with ease and comfort by using this refreshing menthol gel which mildly numbs the throat. www.www.adameve.com

 A&E Oral Sensations Gel... this cool menthol breeze will feel wonderful on either on your tongue and on his cock. www.adameve.com

 Good Head Sampler... receive 5 shots in each flavor passion fruit, cherry spearmint, cinnamon and strawberry. www.holisticwisdom.com

 **Blow Job Kit**... this will delight your lover and advance your Blow Job techniques. You'll be his Head Goddess with the following oral-sex paraphernalia. Sample the Wet Flavored Lube, as you apply the tips and techniques you've become skilled at, in watching Nina Hartley's Guide to Better Fellatio DVD. Caress his cock and balls with the Fukuoku 9000 vibrator that you can also use on your clit while you're orally pleasuring him. And we've added Durex Flavored Condoms if you need to spice it up and keep the sex safe. www.libida.com

~Oral Sex Expert Reading-Repertoire~

 The Ultimate Oral Sex Pocket Guide for Her (Author unknown)... want to blow his mind?... Lots of explicit techniques and tips. This booklet includes .33 oz. ID Juicy Lube and free Sex Mints. Taken from: www.chocolatefantasies.com

 Head Talk by Bella Maydele... a tasteful and fun guide in oral sex instruction. Written to teach and tease at the same time. Really fun illustrations. Taken from: www.chocolatefantasies.com

 Blow Him Away: How to Give Him Mind-Blowing Oral Sex, by Marcie Micheals and Marie Desalle... most people suck performing oral sex," writes Marcy Michaels, and "a simple want of skill and knowledge is to blame." *Blow Him Away* aims to supply that skill and knowledge and teach you how to give your man earth-shaking pleasure. Work out "lazy lips" with kissing exercises such as Saltwater Pump, Monkey Face, and Jug of Plenty.

The Idiot's Pocket Guide to Oral Sex, by Ava Cadel... learn the skilled tricks that every idiot knows when it comes to giving her man Great Head!

The Ultimate Guide to Oral Sex: How to give a man mind-blowing pleasure, by Sonia Borg. Women want to know if they are good at giving a man oral sex, and how to give more pleasure through this intimate act. Men want to know how to ask for this most favored activity. Oral sex is intricate, playful and can give any couple more satisfaction in their lovemaking and in their relationship. Includes 50 tips, tricks and techniques that any woman can master and that will add pleasure and love to this sexiest gift you can give your man. Hot secrets for the ambitious lover, to swallow or not, find the male g-spot, techniques to make him bigger, simultaneous pleasure, if your baby goes baby-soft, and more. Photos are black and white and somewhat risqué, but not x - rated. Taken from: www.chocolatefantasies.com

The Ultimate Guide to Fellatio: How to Go Down on a Man and Give Him Mind-Blowing Pleasure, by Violet Blue... with wit, expertise and an enthusiastic approach, the author dispels myths and delivers concise information on going down on a man. Featuring a complete resource guide to books, videos, illustrations, and websites depicting fellatio, every tip, trick, and technique for giving skilled and unforgettable fellatio is provided. From talking to your partner about fellatio to male pleasure spots and sexual response, Violet Blue covers rimming, shaving, positions, oral sex games for couples, flavored lubricants, sex toys, and a plethora of oral techniques. Taken from: www.chocolatefantasies.com.

Tickle His Pickle by Sadie Allison... so many penises - and no instruction manual. Till now. Sexy and inspiring... honest and provocative... candid and exciting, Tickle His Pickle informs, entertains and reveals the penis secrets women long to know. This unique penis-lovin' guide is bursting with: Over 50 sizzling techniques to master oral lovemaking. Dozens more ways to turn your hands into living sex toys. How to fulfill his biggest erotic fantasies (so he'll beg for more). More than 100 fun, tasteful, titillating illustrations. Secret touching tips for the "Male G-Spot" & other pleasure zones. The world's first penis instruction manual for women who want to rekindle passion, reawaken romance and revive red-hot sex. Includes more than 50 hand and oral love-making techniques with 100 titillating illustrations to guide your learning process. Taken from: www.chocolatefantasies.com

Worship Your Man's Cock!

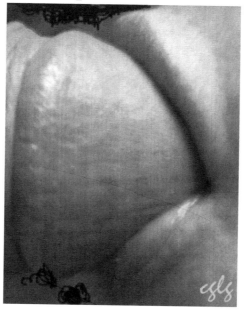

Artist CGLG Artwork featured at: www.eroticalee.com

~Best Give-Your-Man-Great-Head Websites~

The Internet has everything available on every subject... but you need to be careful what you type into a search engine when searching for information on sex, otherwise, you could be swamped with porn you'd rather not view!

When you want to learn more about giving your man Great Head, this is what you need to type into every search engine so that you will get fewer porn sites and more user-friendly instructional sites in your Search List: *1) How to give a Blow Job 2) How to Give Head 3) Advice on how to give a Blow Job.* Below, are a few of the best website on where to get more instruction:

www.alwaysuseacondom.com
www.babeland.com/sexinfo/howto/blow-job
www.dontspitswallow.com
www.holisticwisdom.com
www. howtogivehead.biz
www. howtosuckacock.com
www.sextutor.com

lickhisasslickhisasslickhisasslickhisasslickhisasslickhisasslickh
isasslickhisasslickhisasslickhisasslickhisasslickhisasslickhisass
lickhisasslickhisasslickhisasslickhisasslickhisasslickhisasslickh
isasslickhisasslickhisasslickhisasslickhisasslickhisasslickhisass
lickhisasslickhisasslickhisasslickhisasslickhisasslickhisasslickh
isasslickhisasslickhisasslickhisasslickhisasslickhisasslickhisass
lickhisasslickhisasslickhisasslickhisasslickhisasslickhisasslickh
isasslickhisasslickhisasslickhisasslickhisasslickhisasslickhisass
lickhisasslickhisasslickhisasslickhisasslickhisasslickhisasslickh
isasslickhisasslickhisasslickhisasslickhisasslickhisasslickhisass
lickhisasslickhisasslickhisasslickhisasslickhisasslickhisasslickh
isasslickhisasslickhisasslickhisasslickhisasslickhisasslickhisass

The Dexterity of Bootie Worship

lickhisasslickhisasslickhisasslickhisasslickhisasslickhisasslickh
isasslickhisasslickhisasslickhisasslickhisasslickhisasslickhisass
lickhisasslickhisasslickhisasslickhisasslickhisasslickhisasslickh
isasslickhisasslickhisasslickhisasslickhisasslickhisasslickhisass
lickhisasslickhisasslickhisasslickhisasslickhisasslickhisasslickh
isasslickhisasslickhisasslickhisasslickhisasslickhisasslickhisass
lickhisasslickhisasslickhisasslickhisasslickhisasslickhisasslickh
isasslickhisasslickhisasslickhisasslickhisasslickhisasslickhisass
lickhisasslickhisasslickhisasslickhisasslickhisasslickhisasslickh
isasslickhisasslickhisasslickhisasslickhisasslickhisasslickhisass
lickhisasslickhisasslickhisasslickhisasslickhisasslickhisasslickh
isasslickhisasslickhisasslickhisasslickhisasslickhisasslickhisass
lickhisasslickhisasslickhisasslickhisasslickhisasslickhisasslickh
isasslickhisasslickhisasslickhisasslickhisasslickhisasslickhisass
lickhisasslickhisasslickhisasslickhisasslickhisasslickhisasslickh
isasslickhisasslickhisasslickhisasslickhisasslickhisasslickhisass
lickhisasslickhisasslickhisasslickhisasslickhisasslickhisasslickh
isasslickhisasslickhisasslickhisasslickhisasslickhisasslickhisass
lickhisasslickhisasslickhisasslickhisasslickhisasslickhisasslickh
isasslickhisasslickhisasslickhisasslickhisasslickhisasslickhisass
lickhisasslickhisasslickhisasslickhisasslickhisasslickhisasslickh
isasslickhisasslickhisasslickhisasslickhisasslickhisasslickhisass
lickhisasslickhisasslickhisasslickhisasslickhisasslickhisasslickh
isasslickhisasslickhisasslickhisasslickhisasslickhisasslickhisass
lickhisasslickhisasslickhisasslickhisasslickhisasslickhisasslickh
isasslickhisasslickhisasslickhisasslickhisasslickhisasslickhisass
lickhisasslickhisasslickhisasslickhisasslickhisasslickhisasslickh
isasslickhisasslickhisasslickhisasslickhisasslickhisasslickhisass
lickhisasslickhisasslickhisasslickhisasslickhisasslickhisasslickh
isasslickhisasslickhisasslickhisasslickhisasslickhisasslickhisass
lickhisasslickhisasslickhisasslickhisasslickhisasslickhisasslickh
isasslickhisasslickhisasslickhisasslickhisasslickhisasslickhisass
lickhisasslickhisasslickhisasslickhisasslickhisasslickhisasslickh
isasslickhisasslickhisasslickhisasslickhisasslickhisasslickhisass

VI. The Dexterity of Bootie Worship

*There is hardly anyone whose sexual life,
if it were broadcast, would not fill the
world at large with surprise and horror.*

~~~W. Somerset Maugham

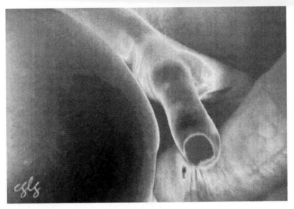

Artist CGLG Artwork featured at: www.eroticalee.com

Ass-fucking and anal play are typically introduced in conversation, books and articles as kinky and taboo. While this portrayal of Anal Sex rouses the imagination of some, the terms kinky and taboo are deterrents to most women.

So - I'll enlighten you on the only two words that accurately describe taking sex with your man to the realm of Ass-Fucking and Anal-Play: *Absolute Power*.

Anal Sex pornography is a staple in the sex-for-sale industry, and it is regularly rented and purchased by the man who *just knows* he will never get it *that way* from the woman he loves.

Your man included.

And part of your man's deviant sexual fascination with ass-fucking pornography, cum-shot magazines and naked dancing girls, *is that he knows he will Absolutely Never get anything like that, from you.*

Pretty daunting thing, Absolutes.

An Absolute can either work for you or work totally against you, depending on which Absolute you choose:

Absolute Power.

Or Absolutely Never.

The simplest route to a man's heart is through his ass. And also through yours.

Absolutely.

~The Art of Anal Sex~

Just like it was when you first learned to walk, Anal Sex begins with trial, error and a lot of blunders - because as uncomplicated as Anal Sex looks in a porn flick, you'll need to remember that unlike the porn actress featured on the film, you have a teeny, tiny little asshole that has never entertained hundreds of meaty cocks! And your man will have some beginner's anxiety as well, since most men lose their erection during their first few attempts at Anal Sex, and he'll need a good, stiff cock to get inside your ass accurately and painlessly.

Because of its immense awkwardness factor, Anal Sex Beginners will have all the sensuality of elephants in a tea room, and it will take more than a few attempts before the two of you get it right. This is why sharing Anal Sex with any man with whom you are not in a reciprocal Romantic Relationship, is truly an ass-backwards choice for you to ever make. So don't.

www.secretgardenpublishing.com

~The Act of Anal Sex~

Start Small and Slow: no matter the size of his cock, you cannot have an object of that magnitude shoved into your ass without a significant amount of pain and discomfort - this is why you need to stretch the opening of your ass before his cock gets anywhere near it. You can start by having him use his fingers to explore and voyage and gently stretch your anal-opening. Make sure his fingernails are clean and cut low, and that he uses lots and lots of thick lubricant that is *specifically* made for Anal Sex. You can find an assortment of this type of lubrication at your local Adult Toy store or on any online sex store via the Internet - and I've put a list of top-quality online Sex stores in the chapter *'Erotic Accessories,'* for easy access to these products.

Before Anal Sex can effortlessly be incorporated into your intimate relationship routine, you need to teach to, and learn from, each other. Taking the time to get it right will decrease you're anxiety and defuse his frustration. Anal Sex is not a first-time-sex-act you can just decide to do on a whim. First-time ass-fucking takes time and preparation and motivation from both of you.

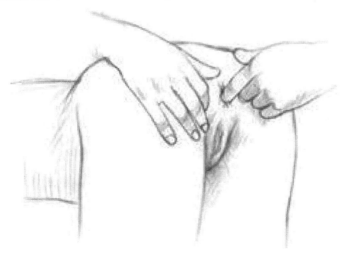

www.secretgardenpublishing.com

Use Bootie Toys: You will find a pictorial-collection of the best Anal Sex Toys (I call them Prostrate Pleasers!) below this section. These bootie toys can be used as instruction tools, as well as for Anal-Sex pleasure. After your ass has become used to the exploration of his fingers, adapt it to the use of any of these well-made Anal Sex toys, before introducing his cock to your ass.

Don't Worry About Shit: The anal canal is not the shit keeper, so you don't have to worry he'll hit a shit wall when he gets inside your ass! If you're concerned that this might happen, you can purchase products like these online:

Anal Douche... cleans-out safely with water. www.babeland.com

Anal Douche... clean up before and after, with this 3" bulb Probe with its 4" Flow Head Attachment. www.adameve.com

Graduation to his Cock: Relaxation Moves are the first step to getting him into your ass: a hot bubble bath, a few glasses of wine, a feather light body massage that flickers between your thighs and stiffens his cock or tranquil vaginal intercourse. When you're ultimately ready to introduce his cock to your ass, just make sure that the opening of your anal-canal is well-lubricated; and it is also imperative that his cock is well-lathered with lubricant as well. If you are still concerned about pain, you can use Anal Sex ointments that contain 9% Benzocain, which will temporarily numb your anal opening and the immediate walls of your rectum. Here are my Top Three picks... but whichever anal-lube you choose to use, *make sure that it is specifically made for Anal Sex*:

Rear Entry... is the perfect lube for orgasmic anal pleasure! This desensitizing lube does double duty: it numbs the anus making penetration easier and helps you stay hard and last longer for unforgettable sex! www.adameve.com.

Moist... use this extra-thick anal lube to turn your anal adventures into a mind-blowing backdoor experience. Sensually super slippery, this water-based lube is non-staining and thicker more long-lasting than most anal lubes. www.adameve.com.

Juice... www.adameve.com's special desensitizing formula is a heavy duty, water-based anal-lube that you can apply as desired before intimate anal-activity. It is one of the best anal lubes on the market, because it does not dry out or become sticky.

Jump Start: The final step, is to find the easiest starter-positions for Anal Sex, which are depicted in explicit photographs directly on the next pages. You will find over one hundred graphically-instructional photographs of Anal Sex from every feasible position, at www.adultcheck.com and from the hand-drawn diagrams that are depicted below, which are featured at www.secretgardenpublishing.com. www.adultcheck.com is the specialist Anal Sex Site because it also demonstrates in pictorial detail, how your man can accomplish better anal-penetration and how to comfortably prepare you for Anal Sex:

Position A) The easiest position for Anal Sex is when you are lying on your side, either curled-up in a fetal position so that your legs are up against your chest, or when your legs are set comfortable into a scissor position.

Position B) Situated doggie-style, this position is most comfortable if you are supported by pillows against and under your tummy and breast, and if your legs are wide-spread as you lean forward.

Position C) Rear entry while you are lying on your tummy.

Position D) Anal-Missionary Position, which is more comfortable if you have a pillow under your buttocks for better support.

~Anal Sex Rules~

1) **Never** switch from Anal Sex then go back to Vaginal Intercourse - you will knock your pussy up with any number of yucky germs and bacteria.

2) **Always** use one of the many Anal Lubes available on the market: Anal Lube is thick and specifically made for Anal Sex. **Never** use standard Vaginal Lube, saliva or your pussy juice for Anal Sex because you'll quickly dry-out and it will hurt **badly**.

3) **Always** wash-up thoroughly after Anal Sex; besides the germ/bacteria factor, sticky lubricants will block the pores in your skin and may cause a pimple outbreak.

4) **Always** clean your Sex Toys without delay after Anal Sex, or you may forget and accidentally put them away germ-infested. You can use anti-bacterial wipes, hand sanitizer or you can wash anything that is not battery-operated in soapy water.

5) **Always** soak your bootie in a hot, soapy bath after Anal Sex, even after you've become a pro at it. A hot bath will clean you out and remove all sticky lubrication and the possibility of breeding bacteria. If you find or feel any cuts or cracks on the outside-entry of your asshole, ask him to gently swath it with Neosporin.

6) **Never** take the Act of Anal Sex for granted... once you've opened that door to him... he's going to be banging relentlessly to Get Back In. Therefore, I suggest that you implement The Reward Method. *You know what I mean.*

www.secretgardenpublishing.com

~His Booty Call~

Anal penetration *isn't* just for girls anymore. Playing Gate-Keeper to *his* ass has long been a principle in many intimate Heterosexual relationships. Most men are clueless to the powerful and intense orgasm that stimulation of their ass will bring, and you can show him what it's all about by easing him into that Great Unknown. Your best bet in introducing your man to the benefits of his booty, is to lead by kissing his ass. Literally.

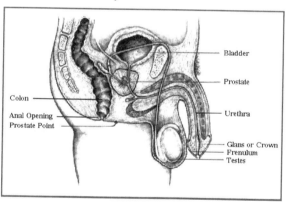

Get to know your man's ass

~The Art of Ass Kissing~

A man naturally assumes that his primary sexual pleasure comes predominantly from his cock. *I assure you that it does not.* The first time you spread your man's ass cheeks and slide your tongue around the pink pucker of his asshole, he will realize sex on a level that overtakes his utmost sexual fantasy. When he cums as you lick that sweetest part of him, it will momentarily obliterate and erase his brain. The experience of cuming like that unbolts a man's emotional lock-box and he will lose emotive control from the pleasure of it. It is *The Act that is That divine and That physically overwhelming.*

Granting your man this technique of extraordinary pleasure makes you a superior lover, and you will put your man in an entirely uncharted sexual stratosphere that will permanently leave your 'mark' on his intimate-psyche.

This is why you never ever want to kiss, lick, taste or deep-rim the ass of a man whom you do not profoundly love, because you will never, ever, ever, ever get rid of him.

There are many ways that you can explore his ass and ascertain what moves your role, as the giver, will bestow on him the greatest pleasure, so, there are no fixed instructions for ass-kissing, there are only suggestions. Once again... you will need to play around with his ass before you'll be on familiar terms with what really does it for him... just make sure that you use lots and lots of lubricant and accept that he will, from *That* point forward, permanently menu this gift from you of Ultimate Sexual Gratification on his Carnal Wall of Desire.

The most comfortable positions for him and for you while kissing his ass, are:

A) He is on the bed or floor on all fours doggie-style, his knees spread and his ass in the air.

B) He is on his back, his legs spread-apart and comfortably wide.

C) He is on his tummy, ass leveled up.

D) He is on the floor, kneeling, leaning into and bent against the seat of a chair, bed or couch, legs spread (not pictured below).

E) He is on his side in a fetal position, knees and legs together, ass tilted for your reach (not pictured below).

F) He is laying/sitting on the couch, legs spread open.

The following photos are courtesy of:
www.assnewcumers.comathome.arcor.de/analingus1/info_en.htm
A. On His Knees...   B. On His Back...   C. On His tummy...

Once he's gotten used to the pleasure of you kissing his ass, the two of you can both explore which sexual positions work best. There are many to choose from and some are more fun and more comfortable than others. Whatever does it for both of you, is what works!

~Ass-Kissing Tricks~

1) Spread his ass cheeks and lick him up-and-down, from his ass-opening to his balls, like you would an ice cream cone, as he strokes his cock until he cums.

2) Nibble around the rim of his ass-opening with your teeth and the twirl your tongue as you dip it in and out of his asshole as he strokes his cock until he cums.

3) Suck the pucker of his asshole into your mouth with a vacuum-like action as you jab your hardened and pointed tongue into the inside of his ass while he strokes his cock until he cums.

4) Suck the pucker his asshole into your mouth with a vacuum-like action as you nibble the rim of his asshole with your teeth, while he strokes his cock until he cums.

5) Bury your mouth into his ass cheeks, and stroke the opening of his ass with your tongue while you pump and stroke the shaft of his cock with your hands until he cums.

6) Soak the crack of his ass with lubricant and then gently slide your clean, short-nailed finger into his ass opening, pressing downward on the prostate gland as your mouth licks and sucks on, above, and below, kissing his ass-cheeks and licking his balls until he cums.

7) Twirl your tongue into his asshole like a power drill, then cup and lightly squeeze his balls with one hand, then with the other hand, cup it around the head of his cock and quickly and gently squeeze the head of his cock in repetitive motion until he cums.

~Ass-Kissing Rules~

1) **Never** kiss the ass of a man with whom you are not in a secure and committed relationship. If you kiss the ass of just any man that you're dating, and he's a guy you only like or feel so-so about, you will **never, ever, ever get rid of him**.

2) **Always** have a pack of anti-bacterial wipes within reach during anal-play, and gently swipe one down-the-crack and into-the-opening of his ass before you dive in with your tongue.

3) **Never** rely on your saliva for lubrication during ass-kissing, **always** have lots of delectable lube within reach and lather it generously on his ass, his balls and his cock.

4) **Always** have baby-wipes within reach, so you can clean off your sticky hands and his sticky nether region after kissing his ass.

5) **Never** kiss his mouth until after you've rinsed-out your mouth with mouthwash. If you want to kiss his mouth in-between kissing his ass, just keep a bottle of mouthwash nearby and take a swig before you kiss him. Since you are the one who is in control, it's easy to kiss his ass and be safe about it.

6) **Always** keep products like Sphincterine on-hand. Sphincterine is an 'asstringent' made specifically for ass-kissing. It gives a tingly sensation and tastes minty fresh, and it can be applied by washcloth or directly on his sphincter or yours. You can find Sphincterine at www.adameve.com.

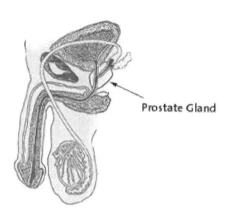

Prostate Gland

~Booty Games~

The diagram above shows you exactly where to arouse his prostate and the products featured below are the best in the Booty business. You can find all of these products on the Internet at the featured online shops listed in the chapter Erotic Accessories:

Aneros Plug... slim for easy insertion and curved to stimulate his prostate gland, this Prostate Pleaser even has a molded handle that you can gently use to apply pressure into his Perineum (the zone between his anal opening and balls). www.babeland.com

Enspiral Anal Plug... twisted for stronger orgasms, this Prostrate Pleaser is 6-inches of rubber that has a stiff inner core that is covered with slick rubber. www.adameve.com

Three Stage Plug... This 5-inch chrome Prostrate Pleaser has a 'solid weight, heavy metal' feel. It's beaded metal and shiny, curvaceous balls easily transmit heat and cold. www.babeland.com

 E-Glass Petite Plug... This 4-inch hand-blown glass plug is a frictionless Prostate Pleaser that quickly heats up to his body temp. www.babeland.com

 Mr. Softee Anal Plug... Pretty in pink all-rubber Prostrate Pleaser; great for beginning booty-worshipers. www.adameve.com

 Tail Light... made of hard acrylic, this clear Prostate Pleaser has a narrow flange that keeps it securely in place. www.babeland.com

 Heavy Metal Buttplug... made of solid metal, this Prostate Pleaser has a silken-sleek outer-coating and will take him into the outer-world of anal bliss. www.babeland.com

 Rosebud Crystal... these diamond like butt plugs are made of heavy weighted stainless steel, and comes in a 4-inch diameter X-Large size only, and weigh a total of 1 pound each. www.babeland.com

 Lil' Devil Butt Plug... this 4-inch Prostate Pleaser is a red Devil tail with a lovely point that with provoke his prostate gland until he cums like every naughty boy should. www.adameve.com

Deluxe Crystal Wand... Only 1-inch thick, this Lucite Prostate Pleaser is tapered with a ripple, and so easily inserted, you can teach your lover how to play with it all by himself. www.babeland.com

 Anal Filler... this Prostate Pleaser has three pleasure balls and a soft jelly shaft. www.adameve.com

 Blue Ribbed Juicer... chunky and unique; this Prostate Pleaser has the form of a 'fruit juice extractor.' www.babeland.com

 Anal Swizzle Stick... with a sure-grip and pure-silicon rubber, this Prostate Pleaser is flexible and sensi-swirled. www.adameve.com

 Anal Screw... Spiral Jelly Prostate Pleaser that sports a corkscrew tip with a tapered magenta shaft. www.adameve.com

 Silicone Ultra Probe... a Prostate Pleaser that is totally bendable and versatile for fast-and-easy anal play. www.adameve.com

 Rocko... a plum-colored, cock-size Realistic with balls, it is a Prostate Pleaser that is curved and firm to hit his spot just right. www.babeland.com

The Excaliber Crystal Sparkler... fancy and sleek two-ended Prostate Pleaser that gives you the option of 5 1/14th long with a 1 ½-inch tapered end or a ridged 4 ½-inch with a 1 1/4th handle. www.adameve.com

Clear Spot G-Probe... the Goliath of Prostate Pleasers and made of Pyrex so that you can use it with water, silicone or oil-based lubes, it is super-smooth and double-ended so that he feels tremendous all over. www.babeland.com

Double Ripple... another Prostate Pleaser made of Pyrex, so that you can use it with any water, silicone or oil-based lube, this super-smooth surface is also double-ended, with one of the tips rippled twice for extended ecstasy. www.babeland.com

Impulse Hypersonic Wand... the only marketed Prostate Pleaser that is ingenious and efficient, it has a built-in computer chip, a hi-tech battery pack, LED display, Ultra-Sensitive controlled pads, a 5-inch wand that is flexible, with a 2 ½-inch head and four Functions of Escalation through accelerated vibration. www.adameve.com

Magic Wand Attachment... this Hitachi Magic Wand is an attachment to any vibrator, and is made of silicon material that is non-porous and designed like a cock with Prostate Pleasing design. www.babeland.com

Serpent's Tail... the silver-bullet base in this Prostrate Pleaser sends vibrations to the tip of this black-vinyl covered vibrator. www.adameve.com

~Porn-Star Pretty Bootie~

Some men really love a woman's dark parts, such as on the insides of her thighs or in the cave between her ass-cheeks. Maybe your man would like to see your inner-ass, what I like to term, "Porn Star Pretty."

A 'Porn Star Pretty' ass is one which the skin has been bleached even and as light as the skin on the rest of her body. This, then, requires special bleaching. Don't worry, because it is safe and easy!

Sex Goddess Keesha Myas explains it best, on her website www.bleachbum.com: *"Anal Bleaching is not something you would want to try without receiving a little advice first. That portion of your body is quite sensitive. Using the wrong product, or any product at all can cause an uncomfortable chemical burn, so you will want to be careful. If however, you would like to bleach your anal area for a younger looking appearance this is probably a great place for you to visit. If you are interested in lightening the skin in your anal area we suggest you try one of three different methods:*

1. You can seek the help of a cosmetic surgeon or dermatologist. They can prescribe a topical treatment. Some treatments are applied in the office by a medical technician, while others are given as a prescription for you to use in the privacy of your own home. This skin bleaching cream may be similar to prescription acne creams Retin-A (tretinoin) or Azelex (azelaic acid). These creams are often prescribed for a condition called Melasma. Melasma are dark discolorations of the skin in patches. So, if you are comfortable seeing a doctor for other procedures, you might ask about a cream for the purpose of anal bleaching.

2. You can seek an over-the-counter skin bleaching cream. A milder skin bleaching cream is an excellent choice. Look for a 2% solution of Hydroquinone as it should be mild enough to use on this delicate area. Often, Hydroquinone creams are used to minimize spots that occur due to sun exposure, age, and birth control pills. For this reason they are often coupled with sunscreens. If you are looking to bleach your anus you DON'T want a product with a sunscreen. Look for a nighttime formula instead.

To effectively bleach your anal area, apply the cream twice a day. You should see gradual results quickly and continuously. You can discontinue use of the cream when you reach your desired, even skin tone. Note: Discontinue use if you suffer any discomfort or if your skin is broken or inflamed in that area.

3. You can prevent anal staining by being cautious in the bathroom. We suggest using a moist wipe after every bowel movement. This will ensure that the area remains clean and stain free. Using a moist wipe is especially important if you are in the process of bleaching that area. Baby wipes can work if you have some handy but you can't flush them. Cottonelle Moist Wipes are probably a better choice for adults. They are flushable. You don't have to worry about clogging your plumbing.

Anal Bleaching is the new Brazilian waxing... at www.shopinprivate.com they looked high and low to find the right product to use to bleach the skin around your anus. It is a 2% hydroquinone formula that is gentle enough for most people to use in sensitive areas.

 Rectal Moist Wipes... www.shopinprivate.com also carries these rectal moist wipes. You will find that they keep your anal area stain free during and after the bleaching process.

~Taboo Sex~

In the October 2004 issue of PLAYBOY magazine, gifted authoress Toni Bentley penned an article titled Taboo Sex, in which she explained the beauty and profound intimacy of experiencing Anal Sex with that One Man. I have paraphrased and condensed her expose for the purpose of this book, but I encourage you to visit www.playboy.com, and order a back-issue of their October 2004 issue so that you can read the entire feature.

I've been a writer for a long time and have read many articles when doing research... and it takes a lot for me to experience something unique... so, when I read Toni Bentley' article Taboo Sex, it really made me appreciate just how intimately-extreme couples can make their monogamous relationship, if they choose to:

~Taboo Sex~

By: Toni Bentley

"His Cock. Enormous. Thick. Unyielding.

My Ass. Unwinding. Divine. Tiny, tight, tightly wound.

You just don't know when he is going to show up. The one who is going to change everything forever, the one who is going to rock your world. The bliss of being sodomized by him is experiencing Eternity in a moment of real time. It is the ultimate act of sexual trust. Being fucked in the ass, he fucks me into femininity. My yearning is so carnivorous, so deep, so old yet so young, that only his big cock buried deep in my ass will fill it. He is that cock. The one that saved me. He is the answer to every man before him. A man who is not afraid. A man who has the balls to fuck me in my tight little asshole.

This is my act of sacrifice, the first that delivers me to an entirely new place instead of a new angle on an old one. I simply wanted to let this particular man into me. I wanted who he was, deep inside who I was. I am, you see, a woman who has been in search of surrender my whole life, to find something, someone, to whom I could subsume my ego, my will. This is the truth about beauty and the power of submission. Anal Sex is about cooperation. One is in charge, the other obedient. It is a high wire act, where pleasure alone is mere a temporary indulgence, a subtle distraction, an anesthetization while on the path to something higher, lower, and deeper. This Eternity lies beyond pleasure. Beyond pain. The edge of my ass is the sexual horizon, the boundary beyond which there is no escape. It rides the edge of insanity. Ass fucking a woman is clearly about authority. The man's authority and the woman's complete acceptance of it. A man must have this confidence, in himself and in his cock, to fuck a woman in the ass. The arrogant man is not a great ass fucker. The great sodomite is patient, gentle and knows how to listen to a woman and be with a woman. He absorbs all that she gives up to him.

He told me once that he likes being where he should not be, crossing the velvet rope, hand in the candy jar, late for work, cock in hand. He makes it deeply into my ass because he dared.

He is the only one who never yields to my will.

Any man who dares to be that intimate, that crazy, gets to go to a place he never got before."

www.secretgardenpublishing.com

The information presented in this chapter is a mere peek into the deity of Anal Sex! For complete details on the benefits of Booty-Worship, you'll want to research the specialists:

~Best Bootie Books~

 The Topping Book... written by Dossie Easton and Janet W. Hardy. Learn how to provide the kind of sensations that all bottoms crave in 'The Topping Book," as well as: how-to keep your bottom safe and bestow hot, spicy interludes.

 The Bottoming Book... written by Dossie Easton and Janet W. Hardy, explains "How to Get Terrible Things Done to You by Wonderful People."

 The Ultimate Guide to Anal Sex for Women... by Tristan Taormino, will give you an inside guide to the benefits of ass- fucking. Hey, if you can't say ass-fucking, you'll never be able to do It!

 Anal Health and Pleasure: A Guide for Men and Women, by Jack Morin, Ph.D... is The Butt Bible. Absolutely. So much information in this book, you'll have to take a written test afterward!

 Naughty Spanking, by Rachel Kramer Bussel... this book has been a huge hit around the office! If you like spanking, are a bit curious, or just want a plethora of spanking ideas to try at home, this well-written and extremely explicit collection of stories from acclaimed authors delivers the goods. I've included this book, because it really shows-off the lighter side, and the fun, of exploring your (and his) bootie.

Best Anal DVD's:

 Nina Hartley's Guide to Anal Sex... with an emphasis on enjoyment, communication and desire, Nina Hartley and three friends (two men and a woman) demonstrate fun, safe anal play. Enjoy explicit demos of pleasurable anal intercourse techniques, along with a basic anatomy lesson. Tips on giving and receiving manual stimulation and analingus, along with information on using sex toys anally.

 The Ultimate Guide to Anal Sex for Women... the DVD version of Tristan Taormino's bestselling book, '*The Ultimate Guide to Anal Sex for Women*', this work features unbelievably arousing anal sex scenes mixed with funny, genuinely enlightening conversations about all things anal. This is something great to watch with him, to break the ice.

 Anal Massage... in this extraordinary DVD, learn the art of anal massage as Dr. Carol Queen and Dr. Robert Lawrence guide you stroke-by-stroke through two and half hours of expert, hands-on demonstrations by professional body workers, sex educators and four real-life couples.

 Anal Massage For Lovers... continuing in the tradition of *Anal Massage for Relaxation and Pleasure*, this DVD hosted by Dr. Carol Queen and Dr. Robert Lawrence, explores the fine art of incorporating anal massage into your lovemaking.

~Best Bootie Websites~

The Internet has everything available on every subject... but you need to be careful what you type into a search engine when searching for information on sex, otherwise, you could be swamped with porn you'd rather not view!

When you want to learn more about Anal Sex or Rimming (ass-kissing), this is what you need to type into every search engine so that you will get fewer porn sites and more user-friendly instructional sites in your Search List:

1) How to have Anal Sex
2) Anal Sex Advice/Instructions
3) Safe Anal Sex
4) What is Rimming
5) Rimming Safely
6) Safe Anal Sex and Rimming.

Below, are a few of the best websites on where to get more instruction:

www.adultcheck.com
www.analsexyes.com
www.anniesprinkle.com
www.allsexguide.com
www.anal-sex-information.com
www.assnewcumers.com
www.keepitkinky.co.uk
www.PuckerUp.com (features The Anal Advisor column written by expert Analist Ms. Tristan Taormino)

~Superb sex is sex that is always atypical~

```
strokehiscockstrokehiscockstrokehiscockstrokehiscockstrokehiscock
strokehiscockstrokehiscockstrokehiscockstrokehiscockstrokehiscock
strokehiscockstrokehiscockstrokehiscockstrokehiscockstrokehiscock
strokehiscockstrokehiscockstrokehiscockstrokehiscockstrokehiscock
strokehiscockstrokehiscockstrokehiscockstrokehiscockstrokehiscock
strokehiscockstrokehiscockstrokehiscockstrokehiscockstrokehiscock
strokehiscockstrokehiscockstrokehiscockstrokehiscockstrokehiscock
strokehiscockstrokehiscockstrokehiscockstrokehiscockstrokehiscock
strokehiscockstrokehiscockstrokehiscockstrokehiscockstrokehiscock
strokehiscockstrokehiscockstrokehiscockstrokehiscockstrokehiscock
strokehiscockstrokehiscockstrokehiscockstrokehiscockstrokehiscock
strokehiscockstrokehiscockstrokehiscockstrokehiscockstrokehiscock
```

Goddess Hand Enchantments

```
strokehiscockstrokehiscockstrokehiscockstrokehiscockstrokehiscock
strokehiscockstrokehiscockstrokehiscockstrokehiscockstrokehiscock
strokehiscockstrokehiscockstrokehiscockstrokehiscockstrokehiscock
strokehiscockstrokehiscockstrokehiscockstrokehiscockstrokehiscock
strokehiscockstrokehiscockstrokehiscockstrokehiscockstrokehiscock
strokehiscockstrokehiscockstrokehiscockstrokehiscockstrokehiscock
strokehiscockstrokehiscockstrokehiscockstrokehiscockstrokehiscock
strokehiscockstrokehiscockstrokehiscockstrokehiscockstrokehiscock
strokehiscockstrokehiscockstrokehiscockstrokehiscockstrokehiscock
strokehiscockstrokehiscockstrokehiscockstrokehiscockstrokehiscock
strokehiscockstrokehiscockstrokehiscockstrokehiscockstrokehiscock
strokehiscockstrokehiscockstrokehiscockstrokehiscockstrokehiscock
strokehiscockstrokehiscockstrokehiscockstrokehiscockstrokehiscock
strokehiscockstrokehiscockstrokehiscockstrokehiscockstrokehiscock
strokehiscockstrokehiscockstrokehiscockstrokehiscockstrokehiscock
strokehiscockstrokehiscockstrokehiscockstrokehiscockstrokehiscock
strokehiscockstrokehiscockstrokehiscockstrokehiscockstrokehiscock
strokehiscockstrokehiscockstrokehiscockstrokehiscockstrokehiscock
strokehiscockstrokehiscockstrokehiscockstrokehiscockstrokehiscock
strokehiscockstrokehiscockstrokehiscockstrokehiscockstrokehiscock
strokehiscockstrokehiscockstrokehiscockstrokehiscockstrokehiscock
strokehiscockstrokehiscockstrokehiscockstrokehiscockstrokehiscock
strokehiscockstrokehiscockstrokehiscockstrokehiscockstrokehiscock
strokehiscockstrokehiscockstrokehiscockstrokehiscockstrokehiscock
strokehiscockstrokehiscockstrokehiscockstrokehiscockstrokehiscock
strokehiscockstrokehiscockstrokehiscockstrokehiscockstrokehiscock
strokehiscockstrokehiscockstrokehiscockstrokehiscockstrokehiscock
strokehiscockstrokehiscockstrokehiscockstrokehiscockstrokehiscock
strokehiscockstrokehiscockstrokehiscockstrokehiscockstrokehiscock
strokehiscockstrokehiscockstrokehiscockstrokehiscockstrokehiscock
strokehiscockstrokehiscockstrokehiscockstrokehiscockstrokehiscock
strokehiscockstrokehiscockstrokehiscockstrokehiscockstrokehiscock
strokehiscockstrokehiscockstrokehiscockstrokehiscockstrokehiscock
strokehiscockstrokehiscockstrokehiscockstrokehiscockstrokehiscock
strokehiscockstrokehiscockstrokehiscockstrokehiscockstrokehiscock
strokehiscockstrokehiscockstrokehiscockstrokehiscockstrokehiscock
strokehiscockstrokehiscockstrokehiscockstrokehiscockstrokehiscock
strokehiscockstrokehiscockstrokehiscockstrokehiscockstrokehiscock
strokehiscockstrokehiscockstrokehiscockstrokehiscockstrokehiscock
```

VII. Goddess Hand Enchantments

Lovemaking with a beautiful and generous woman,
performed with careful attention,
is the best medicine of all.

~~~Sushruta Samhita

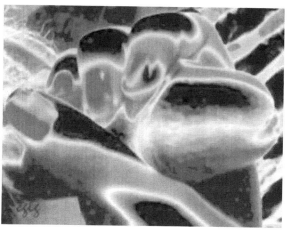

Artist CGLG Artwork featured at: www.eroticalee.com

Your hand and your caress reveal more about you than you may have previously considered. How you touch your man shows more to him in regard to how you really feel about him, above any declaration of love or adoration that you will ever utter to him. When you touch his cock, this is how he hears and sees that you love him, want him, need him.

Giving a man sex via a Hand-Job is usually a Sex Act that's performed by a woman at the beginning of a relationship... before she gives him Head or moves-on to sexual intercourse with him... so giving a man a Hand-Job becomes a Sex Act that is rarely done after a relationship has settled into a comfortable, sexual routine.

Which is really too bad! Because giving your man a Hand Job can be just as sweet a treat as anything else you do to his bod!

It's easy to re-learn the sexual value and erotic importance of giving your man a Hand-Job, and to once again incorporate your sexy hand moves back into the magic of your sexual relationship with your man. It will give your man extraordinary pleasure that will earn you the title of a superior lover in his eyes.

~How to Give Your Man a Luxury Hand Job~

Try-out any of the following Luxury Hand Moves, or be inventive and make-up a few of your own. Just touch your man. He will adore you for it.

*The Twister:

*lube-up both of your hands.

*place one hand on each side of his cock.

*slide one hand upward toward the head of his cock, while you move your other hand downward to the base of his cock.

*grip his cock tightly with both hands, and then quickly twist his cock inside both of your hands, keeping your upward-hand under the head of his cock, and your down-ward hand firmly on the base of his cock.

*keep twisting steadily until he cums.

*The Pearl Wrap:

*lube-up his cock.

*take a long string of unclasped faux-pearls and wrap them from the head of his cock to the base of his cock, leaving enough length on both ends so that you can re-fasten the clasp.

*envelope the pearls with one of your hands, and gently stroke his cock with heavy-light pressure and a very slow-quick variation of speed.

*The Swizzle:

*lube-up both of your hands.

*place your right hand on the top of his cock and stroke downward.

*before your right hand gets-to the base of his cock, place your left hand on the head of his cock and stroke downward.

*as your left hand reaches your right hand, quickly move your right hand to the head of his cock as your left hand reaches the base of his cock.

*continue to swizzle-stroke your hands on his cock until he cums.

*The Oil Spill:

*sit naked behind him, with your breasts and pussy pressed against his naked back and ass. This works better if your naked back is supported against a couch, steady chair or secure bed frame.

*slide your arms around his waist and lean his neck into the crook of yours. Gently spread his legs so that you have full-cock access, and then bring your legs up. Bend at the knee and tighten your legs against the side of his back.

*soak both of your hands in lubricant.

*if you are right-handed, slide your left hand under his balls, while you stroke his cock with your right hand (switch hands on this if you're a Lefty).

*while one hand cradles his balls and the other hand strokes his cock, press your lips into his neck and kiss him and lick him, or, use this opportunity to softly tell him a truly nasty sex story.

*keep stroking his cock until his cums spills over your hands.

*The Shaken Soda:

*lube-up both of your hands.

*grip him underneath the head of his cock with one hand.

*slide your other hand between the crack of his ass, and slowly massage his rectal-area.

*begin to shake and pump his cock with your grip only underneath the head of his cock.

*take your thumb after you've begun, and use it as a gauge, pressing and releasing, pressing and releasing into the little hole in the head of his cock.

*just as he begins to cum, slam your thumb onto that little hole, like you'd slam a tack into a wall, as you continue to pump his cock.

*The Silken Cord:

*lay him on his back.

*slide your hands around his nether-regions until you've gotten him nice and hard.

*take a silken handkerchief or a very wide silken hair ribbon and twist it into a cord.

*wrap the twisted silken cord twice, half-way around the shaft of his cock, leaving both end of the silken cord free, and then pull the silken-cord tight. Suck the head of his cock while both your hands keep hold of both ends of the silken-cord.

*each time he starts to cum... and if he can hold-on without losing his mind... stop and re-start his climax three times.

*just as he begins to explode cum, let go of the silken cord with one hand, and yank it off his cock with the other.

~Great Hand-Stroking Tips~

*Always position him so that both of you are comfortable when you give him a Hand Job.

*Always use a light touch or a firm grip, depending on his mood or what he likes. He'll be sure to tell you how he wants it as soon as you begin.

*Always make sure as you stroke his cock, that you use full, long and steady strokes. Your consistent cock-stroking rhythm is very important, because if you break-rhythm, you will set-back his climax and his cuming-aura.

*Always pay attention to his body movements and what he says or how he is moaning or groaning... and then accelerate your cock-stroking as his breathing changes and he becomes more excited.

*Always pay close attention to his breathing - when he's about to cum he will take shallower and shallower breaths.

*When giving him a basic Hand Job, end it with a gentle tug on his balls or by rubbing the outside of his anus in a circular motion with your forefinger.

www.secretgardenpublishing.com

Best Hand-Job Positions

1) You can seat-position him on the couch with his feet-flat on the floor while your entire body is between his legs.

2) You can seat-position him on the couch, with his ass slightly elevated and his feet on the couch cushion, with your head and shoulders between his legs.

3) You can either seat-position him or half-way lay-position him against a pile of soft pillows on your bed, with your head and shoulders between his legs for easy access.

4) You can lay him completely flat (no pillow!) on your bed or on the floor.

5) You can put his hands against the shower wall as you reach between his legs in the shower.

6) You can place a bath pillow under his head or a body-bath pillow under his back and neck as you stroke his cock in the bath.

7) You can shift his lower body slightly-forward as you reach for his cock to stroke him while he's driving the car.

~Ball Play~

*Lube your hand and gently roll his balls inside your palm, as you would a pair of Asian Relaxation Balls.

*Gently suck one or both of his balls into your mouth and massage them with your tongue as you roll them against your cheeks.

*Lightly trace his balls with your fingernails; stroke his balls with a feather, or fondle his balls with silky pair of panties.

*'Nut Drum' his balls by using your forefinger and thumb to tighten his scrotum-skin, then gently tap, tap, tap his balls with a finger from your other hand.

~Best Hand-Job Lubrication Tips~

*KY Jelly dries-out quickly. You're better-off using a glob of Petroleum-based Vaseline. KY is the *worst* lubricant on-the-market... it will get tacky and sticky and that is no fun! So NO KY!

*Never rely on your saliva; not only will you never be able to produce enough quickly enough to keep the Hand-Job sweet-n-steady, but it also dries out very quickly. Another point: dried-out saliva doesn't smell very nice, either.

*Make sure that you use a lot of lubrication when giving him a Hand-Job... because the slickness of the lubrication in your hand as you steadily-stroke his cock, is what causes the heated-friction that makes him cum.

*Never use flowery-floral, fruity-sweet or candy-sugary scented lubrications when giving your man a Hand Job. Smell is a huge factor when it comes to seduction.

*Always use a down-to-earth or natural scented lubricant; these types of lubricants are what arouse your man the most.

*Always: if you're in-doubt about what to use because you don't have any of the above-mentioned or featured-below types of lubricants on-hand, you're better off just using a clear/natural/scentless lubricant.

~Outstanding Cock Creams and Lubricants~

If you want to be **The Cock Queen**, than do your hand magic on him by using one of these boy-products whenever you stroke his cock.

The following Hand-Job products listed below produce better cum results than regular lotions, oils or lubes when used for masturbation... because they are *specifically* made for The Man and His Cock... and are the only types of lubrication you should use when giving your man Goddess Hand Job.

 Stroke 29... this thick, creamy lubricant takes on the "heat and glide of aroused human tissue." The heavy, face-cream consistency stays exactly where you put it, but becomes slippery with use, adding delicious friction without being so wet you'll lose your grip on him. It's long lasting. www.babeland.com

 Boy Butter... spreads on with ease, lasts a long time, and washes off with plain water. *Oils in the cream make it incompatible with latex condoms and with vaginas*, but if you stroke his cock with this, he will be screaming your name. Just remember: use a wipe on his cock before he takes a dip inside your pussy! www.babeland.com

Gun Oil Lubricant... was developed by lonely, horny soldiers in the field, and it is a silicone-based Gun Oil that is thick, super-slippery and long-lasting. This lube is magnificent for giving him hand jobs, because, well, it was invented by lonely, horny soldiers in the field!! You can use it with condoms and your pretty pussy - so get some! www.babeland.com

~Magnificent Masturbators~

Sometimes, the best Hand Job you'll ever give him is the thrill and adventure you can add to the routine.

There are so many specialty adult toys and pleasurable masturbation devices on-the-market, you're sure to find one that will make you a gold medalist in Cock-Stroking.

 The Senso Glowing Pussy... is the unsurpassed, extraordinary super-stretchy ribbed masturbator sleeve that fits him like a glove. Easy stretch to fit any man!

 Mouth Job... wickedly soft, stretchy and ribbed silicone SENSO material; its 5 inches expand and contract around any size penis for tight sensation. 2 rows of embedded pleasure beads ripple along cock shaft for one unforgettable orgasm after another! Use with water-based lube. www.adameve.com

Jessica Drake Pussy... this soft, pink pussy is modeled on the real-life love grotto of Wicked Girl, so slide his cock inside it and he'll feel the incredible fleshy sensations of the unique Futurotic™ material... mmm! Durable and long-lasting, its compact size makes it convenient to take anywhere or simply use in the comfort of your home. www.adameve.com

Cock Masturbator... fits like a second skin. This super-stretchy silicone masturbator is crystal clear and penis shaped for visual excitement. It is open-ended for easy clean-up. www.adameve.com

 The Anal Tunnel... has rows of soft inner rings to stroke his shaft and grip him like a woman's tight ass, with soft nubs that enthrall him into climax! www.adameve.com

 The Love Tunnel... is a two-toned jelly masturbator that comfortably fits into your hand and stretches to accommodate any man. It features a pussy-like opening, with rows and rows of soft inner rings that slide around his cock for magnificent sensation. www.adameve.com

~The Internet Hand-Job Goddess~

I have much awe and admiration for Keesha Myas... she runs the site www.handJobAdvice.com... and it is such a brilliant idea that I just want to give her a Hand-Job Medal or maybe a Golden Dildo! This is a free, instructional video-based website that provides lessons on how to give your man a great Hand Job. Keesha uses several different dildos (no nudity!) and shows you, via about 30 short videos (including sound) how to give your man a delicious hand job! Check-out the definitions of each Hand-Job that Keesha's demonstrates, pick-out the one's you'd like to try on your man, and then go online to www.handJobAdvice.com and watch the illustrated video!

Here is Keesha's Expert Hand-Job Video List:

~The Squeezing Ring: This site must show you at least 20 different ways to give a hand job. You will probably want to try a few of them yourself. If you find yourself stopping to think of something new, give him the squeezing ring to keep it all going strong.

~*The Pancake*: This hand job method is a good way to start and a great way to apply lube to your man, you might want to give it a go.

~*Washing Machine*: This is one of the best methods to learn if you want to give an awesome hand job. In fact, if you are only going to learn one technique from this website, it should be the washing machine. So watch the above video and see what everyone is talking about.

~*Endless Tunnel*: This is a great hand job method because it will remind him of how much he wants to make love to you. So, if you want to give your guy a surprise hand job but don't want him to be finished for the night, try out the endless tunnel.

~*2-Finger Corkscrew*: You probably already know this technique. Heck, it is probably what you do naturally, but our advice is to move your elbow back and forth. That is where the corkscrew action comes from: the elbow.

~*Milking The Bull*: This isn't how they do it down on the farm, but your stud will be sure to love this hand job method. So watch this short video and your man can send us a personal thank you letter for our advice.

~*Starting A Fire*: You probably don't know how to start a fire in the woods with two sticks and I can't teach you how. I don't know either. I do know this technique for giving a hand job and it is called starting a fire.

~*The Doorknob*: Your man probably won't sound too interested in any move that has you twisting the top of his penis like a doorknob, so use plenty of lube for this one. The more lube you use the more he will like it.

~*The Palm Lick*: This hand job technique teaches you to use your palm as if it were a big tongue.

~*Fakie Hand-Job*: The name for the fakie hand job comes from snowboarding or skateboarding. Fakie refers to riding backward. Well, the fakie hand job has you using your hand backward. See the video above for a new piece of hand job advice.

~*Swizzle Stick*: Named after those things you use to stir a drink, I am sure that your man will find the swizzle stick hand job method to be quite tasty.

~*Over/Under*: Watch this video and you will learn a technique that concentrates on the most sensitive areas of the penis. This technique, that we call the over-under hand job will be a big hit.

~*The Shocker*: Some guys might like a little bit of a finger in the bum. If you wonder if your guy would, just put a finger in that area and see if he protests, if doesn't lube up a finger and push it upward and toward the spot behind his penis. There is a gland in there called the prostate. If you massage it, he'll go nuts.

~*Wild Butterfly*: The wild butterfly hand job technique is a good way to start a hand job. You use your fingers as if they were bristles in a paint brush. Gently brush up and down the sides, top and bottom of your partner's penis. This will get him going.

~*The Flattener*: If your man likes his hand jobs on the firm side, perhaps you should try the flattener on him. It will be a new and unique sensation for him and he will probably like it. A lot.

~*Ping Pong*: This method is as much mental as it is physical, make your man feel huge by using is penis for a game of side-to-side catch. I call it the ping-pong method although you won't want to use a paddle.

~*The Healing Stroke*: Everyone deserves a great hand job even people that may have trouble getting a great erection. The healing stroke can be used to keep that erection going strong. We hope you will give it a try.

~*The Slippy Grippy*: This is a good move to do to end the hand job. Everything else you have learned leads up to the slippy grippy. The slippy grippy technique will give your man a really, really powerful orgasm.

~*Headless Hand Job*: Most guys seem to like a bit of a tease, so here is a satisfying way to do it. We all know that the head of the penis is the most sensitive area, so why not ignore it. This video shows you how.

~*Two-Handed Slammer*: call this one the double handed slammer or 2 handed slammer. It uses two hands to give a hand job. Watch the short video to see why this is a good idea. Trust me, it is.

~*The Switch Hitter*: Now is your chance to show off a few of the hand job techniques that you learned on www.handJobAdvice.com. The Switch Hitter combines two of them, the fakie hand job and the 2 finger corkscrew but you can combine all of them.

Keesha also shows you, via video, the best-lubes for the job, effective ways to lube-him-up, where his sensitive areas are and how to grip him when you're giving him a Hand Job.

~Best Hand-Job Websites~

The Internet has everything available on every subject... but you need to be careful what you type into a search engine when searching for information on sex, otherwise, you could be swamped with porn you'd rather not view! When you want to learn more about giving your man a good Hand-Job, this is what you need to type into every search engine so that you will get less porn sites and more user-friendly instructional sites in your Search List

1) How to give a Hand Job
2) Advice on how-to give a Hand Job.

Below are a few of the best websites on where to get more instruction:

www.a2zmasturbation.com
www.alwaysuseaCondom.com
www.experts.about.com
www.faq-site.com
www.handJobAdvice.com
www.masturbation-techniques.net
www.sextutor.com
www.sexuality.org

whywhywhywhywhywhywhywhywhywhywhywhywhywhywhywhywhywhywhywhywhywhywh
ywhywhywhywhywhywhywhywhywhywhywhywhywhywhywhywhywhywhywhywhywhywhyw
hywhywhywhywhywhywhywhywhywhywhywhywhywhywhywhywhywhywhywhywhywhywhy
whywhywhywhywhywhywhywhywhywhywhywhywhywhywhywhywhywhywhywhywhywhywh
ywhywhywhywhywhywhywhywhywhywhywhywhywhywhywhywhywhywhywhywhywhywhyw
hywhywhywhywhywhywhywhywhywhywhywhywhywhywhywhywhywhywhywhywhywhywhy
whywhywhywhywhywhywhywhywhywhywhywhywhywhywhywhywhywhywhywhywhywhywh
ywhywhywhywhywhywhywhywhywhywhywhywhywhywhywhywhywhywhywhywhywhywhyw
hywhywhywhywhywhywhywhywhywhywhywhywhywhywhywhywhywhywhywhywhywhywhy
whywhywhywhywhywhywhywhywhywhywhywhywhywhywhywhywhywhywhywhywhywhywh
ywhywhywhywhywhywhywhywhywhywhywhywhywhywhywhywhywhywhywhywhywhywhyw
hywhywhywhywhywhywhywhywhywhywhywhywhywhywhywhywhywhywhywhywhywhywhy
whywhywhywhywhywhywhywhywhywhywhywhywhywhywhywhywhywhywhywhywhywhywh
ywhywhywhywhywhywhywhywhywhywhywhywhywhywhywhywhywhywhywhywhywhywhyw
hywhywhywhywhywhywhywhywhywhywhywhywhywhywhywhywhywhywhywhywhywhywhy

The End of Making Love: The Why

whywhywhywhywhywhywhywhywhywhywhywhywhywhywhywhywhywhywhywhywhywhywh
ywhywhywhywhywhywhywhywhywhywhywhywhywhywhywhywhywhywhywhywhywhywhyw
hywhywhywhywhywhywhywhywhywhywhywhywhywhywhywhywhywhywhywhywhywhywhy
whywhywhywhywhywhywhywhywhywhywhywhywhywhywhywhywhywhywhywhywhywhywh
ywhywhywhywhywhywhywhywhywhywhywhywhywhywhywhywhywhywhywhywhywhywhyw
hywhywhywhywhywhywhywhywhywhywhywhywhywhywhywhywhywhywhywhywhywhywhy
whywhywhywhywhywhywhywhywhywhywhywhywhywhywhywhywhywhywhywhywhywhywh
ywhywhywhywhywhywhywhywhywhywhywhywhywhywhywhywhywhywhywhywhywhywhyw
hywhywhywhywhywhywhywhywhywhywhywhywhywhywhywhywhywhywhywhywhywhywhy
whywhywhywhywhywhywhywhywhywhywhywhywhywhywhywhywhywhywhywhywhywhywh
ywhywhywhywhywhywhywhywhywhywhywhywhywhywhywhywhywhywhywhywhywhywhyw
hywhywhywhywhywhywhywhywhywhywhywhywhywhywhywhywhywhywhywhywhywhywhy
whywhywhywhywhywhywhywhywhywhywhywhywhywhywhywhywhywhywhywhywhywhywh
ywhywhywhywhywhywhywhywhywhywhywhywhywhywhywhywhywhywhywhywhywhywhyw
hywhywhywhywhywhywhywhywhywhywhywhywhywhywhywhywhywhywhywhywhywhywhy
whywhywhywhywhywhywhywhywhywhywhywhywhywhywhywhywhywhywhywhywhywhywh
ywhywhywhywhywhywhywhywhywhywhywhywhywhywhywhywhywhywhywhywhywhywhyw
hywhywhywhywhywhywhywhywhywhywhywhywhywhywhywhywhywhywhywhywhywhywhy
whywhywhywhywhywhywhywhywhywhywhywhywhywhywhywhywhywhywhywhywhywhywh
ywhywhywhywhywhywhywhywhywhywhywhywhywhywhywhywhywhywhywhywhywhywhyw
hywhywhywhywhywhywhywhywhywhywhywhywhywhywhywhywhywhywhywhywhywhywhy
whywhywhywhywhywhywhywhywhywhywhywhywhywhywhywhywhywhywhywhywhywhywh
ywhywhywhywhywhywhywhywhywhywhywhywhywhywhywhywhywhywhywhywhywhywhyw
hywhywhywhywhywhywhywhywhywhywhywhywhywhywhywhywhywhywhywhywhywhywhy
whywhywhywhywhywhywhywhywhywhywhywhywhywhywhywhywhywhywhywhywhywhywh
ywhywhywhywhywhywhywhywhywhywhywhywhywhywhywhywhywhywhywhywhywhywhyw
hywhywhywhywhywhywhywhywhywhywhywhywhywhywhywhywhywhywhywhywhywhywhy
whywhywhywhywhywhywhywhywhywhywhywhywhywhywhywhywhywhywhywhywhywhywh
ywhywhywhywhywhywhywhywhywhywhywhywhywhywhywhywhywhywhywhywhywhywhyw
hywhywhywhywhywhywhywhywhywhywhywhywhywhywhywhywhywhywhywhywhywhywhy
whywhywhywhywhywhywhywhywhywhywhywhywhywhywhywhywhywhywhywhywhywhywh
ywhywhywhywhywhywhywhywhywhywhywhywhywhywhywhywhywhywhywhywhywhywhyw
hywhywhywhywhywhywhywhywhywhywhywhywhywhywhywhywhywhywhywhywhywhywhy
whywhywhywhywhywhywhywhywhywhywhywhywhywhywhywhywhywhywhywhywhywhywh
ywhywhywhywhywhywhywhywhywhywhywhywhywhywhywhywhywhywhywhywhywhywhyw
hywhywhywhywhywhywhywhywhywhywhywhywhywhywhywhywhywhywhywhywhywhywhy
whywhywhywhywhywhywhywhywhywhywhywhywhywhywhywhywhywhywhywhywhywhywh
ywhywhywhywhywhywhywhywhywhywhywhywhywhywhywhywhywhywhywhywhywhywhyw

VIII. The End of Making Love: The Why

There's this place in me where your fingerprints still rest, your kisses still linger, and your whispers softly echo. It's the place where a part of you will forever be a part of me.

~~~Gretchen Kemp

Artwork featured at: www.secretgardenpublishing.com

It was evident from the beginning of my career, that the women who wrote to me seeking my advice concerning the emotional turmoil in their romantic relationships, at some point in those romantic relationships, had relinquished their devotion in Making Love to their man as an expression of passion for him and the taking of pleasure in him, to that of a bargaining chip and a ruse to use in opposition of him.

What predominantly alarmed me as the letters steadily came and the years continued to progress, was that while the overall circumstances were frequently different, the end results were always the same: sweet glistening love had eroded into a decayed contaminated indifference, and Making Love to their man was demoted to merely sex with Just Him, and another have-to in their romantic relationship.

Each of the women who came to me for advice felt a permanent emotional disconnection from their man, but none of these women understood *The Why* that had proceeded that emotional disconnection, and what complicated my quest in seeking to identify this dilemma that was happening to so many woman in their romantic relationships, was that I researched books and articles published by countless relationship experts who knew a great deal more than I did, and never once did I find a single reference from one of those experts to even as much as a recognition of *The Why*, let alone an answer to it.

Long after these letters from women seeking my advice on how to repair the loss-of-intimacy in their romantic relationships had filled my post office box and email address, I became very involved in a serious romantic relationship; the first, since my days in college. One evening my man did *that something* for about the zillionth time, and this feeling within me came from the inside out, and contemptuously erupted. He never listened, he never understood, he had the brain of a genius and the common sense of a moron, and I was going to make him pay until he finally fucking got it.

The angry words that I spewed at him were out of my mouth and set-off, and as I stabbed my anger repeatedly into his heart, *as I saw the look on his face*, I unexpectedly identified *The Why*: that there *is* a turning point in every romantic relationship where the woman makes a conscience choice to sever the intimate connection she has with her man, and make that connection into a bargaining chip and a ruse to use in opposition of him. It is no longer in sweetness and devotion that she Makes Love to him, but *in anger, in blame, and even in hate.*

From the moment a woman chooses in anger, blame, frustration, and loathing, to sever that bond- of-intimacy, everything she does with her man in their physical relationship becomes encrusted by her female poison as it gradually leaks into her heart and contaminates her love for him. I have traced this choice of the woman and the demise of her romantic relationship, as far back as a pile of sweaty underwear, t-shirt and dirty socks that her husband had dropped onto a recently mopped bathroom floor one too many times.

Every woman knows that it is much easier to spew her female poison at a man than to own-up to what it will take to extract it. What most women have never understood, is that this is *The Why* of the loss-of-intimacy in their romantic relationships.

The world is full of men, and their many manly transgressions are as common in every romantic relationship as a cold in winter.

Men don't call when they are supposed to. Men toss their brown-tracked underwear on the floor instead of taking time to make it into a laundry basket. Men don't want to miss a poker night with the boys because their sweetie has the flu. Men feed the kids pizza and soda and allow them to stay up too late on a school night. Men can memorize every NBA team score that is flashed on Fox Sports, yet they never remember how many boxes of juice to pick-up from the grocery store, even when it is written down on a detailed list. Every woman adds-up her man's transgressions, and when she has finally had enough, she severs the emotional bond she has with her man in the bedroom. She brings all her female poison; her anger and frustration and her blame and loathing, and she lays it on the bed between herself and her man. Gradually, over time, sweet glistening love erodes into decayed contaminated indifference.

Keep your female poison out of the bedroom. It is *The Why* of the loss-of-intimacy in your romantic relationship. You can find so many clever ways to make him understand what you need from him without irreversibly damaging that intimate bond.

Women are the reason love happens.

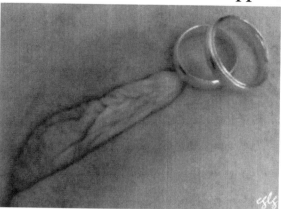

Artist CGLG Artwork featured at: www.eroticalee.com

We are increasingly the reason why it ends.

masturbatemasturbatemasturbatemasturbatemasturbatemasturbatemastu
rbatemasturbatemasturbatemasturbatemasturbatemasturbatemasturbate
masturbatemasturbatemasturbatemasturbatemasturbatemasturbatemastu
rbatemasturbatemasturbatemasturbatemasturbatemasturbatemasturbate
masturbatemasturbatemasturbatemasturbatemasturbatemasturbatemastu
rbatemasturbatemasturbatemasturbatemasturbatemasturbatemasturbate
masturbatemasturbatemasturbatemasturbatemasturbatemasturbatemastu
rbatemasturbatemasturbatemasturbatemasturbatemasturbatemasturbate
masturbatemasturbatemasturbatemasturbatemasturbatemasturbatemastu
rbatemasturbatemasturbatemasturbatemasturbatemasturbatemasturbate
masturbatemasturbatemasturbatemasturbatemasturbatemasturbatemastu
rbatemasturbatemasturbatemasturbatemasturbatemasturbatemasturbate

Your Personal Bliss

masturbatemasturbatemasturbatemasturbatemasturbatemasturbatemastu
rbatemasturbatemasturbatemasturbatemasturbatemasturbatemasturbate
masturbatemasturbatemasturbatemasturbatemasturbatemasturbatemastu
rbatemasturbatemasturbatemasturbatemasturbatemasturbatemasturbate
masturbatemasturbatemasturbatemasturbatemasturbatemasturbatemastu
rbatemasturbatemasturbatemasturbatemasturbatemasturbatemasturbate
masturbatemasturbatemasturbatemasturbatemasturbatemasturbatemastu
rbatemasturbatemasturbatemasturbatemasturbatemasturbatemasturbate
masturbatemasturbatemasturbatemasturbatemasturbatemasturbatemastu
rbatemasturbatemasturbatemasturbatemasturbatemasturbatemasturbate
masturbatemasturbatemasturbatemasturbatemasturbatemasturbatemastu
rbatemasturbatemasturbatemasturbatemasturbatemasturbatemasturbate
masturbatemasturbatemasturbatemasturbatemasturbatemasturbatemastu
rbatemasturbatemasturbatemasturbatemasturbatemasturbatemasturbate
masturbatemasturbatemasturbatemasturbatemasturbatemasturbatemastu
rbatemasturbatemasturbatemasturbatemasturbatemasturbatemasturbate
masturbatemasturbatemasturbatemasturbatemasturbatemasturbatemastu
rbatemasturbatemasturbatemasturbatemasturbatemasturbatemasturbate
masturbatemasturbatemasturbatemasturbatemasturbatemasturbatemastu
rbatemasturbatemasturbatemasturbatemasturbatemasturbatemasturbate
masturbatemasturbatemasturbatemasturbatemasturbatemasturbatemastu
rbatemasturbatemasturbatemasturbatemasturbatemasturbatemasturbate
masturbatemasturbatemasturbatemasturbatemasturbatemasturbatemastu
rbatemasturbatemasturbatemasturbatemasturbatemasturbatemasturbate
masturbatemasturbatemasturbatemasturbatemasturbatemasturbatemastu
rbatemasturbatemasturbatemasturbatemasturbatemasturbatemasturbate
masturbatemasturbatemasturbatemasturbatemasturbatemasturbatemastu
rbatemasturbatemasturbatemasturbatemasturbatemasturbatemasturbate
masturbatemasturbatemasturbatemasturbatemasturbatemasturbatemastu
rbatemasturbatemasturbatemasturbatemasturbatemasturbatemasturbate
masturbatemasturbatemasturbatemasturbatemasturbatemasturbatemastu
rbatemasturbatemasturbatemasturbatemasturbatemasturbatemasturbate
masturbatemasturbatemasturbatemasturbatemasturbatemasturbatemastu
rbatemasturbatemasturbatemasturbatemasturbatemasturbatemasturbate
masturbatemasturbatemasturbatemasturbatemasturbatemasturbatemastu
rbatemasturbatemasturbatemasturbatemasturbatemasturbatemasturbate
masturbatemasturbatemasturbatemasturbatemasturbatemasturbatemastu
rbatemasturbatemasturbatemasturbatemasturbatemasturbatemasturbate
masturbatemasturbatemasturbatemasturbatemasturbatemasturbatemastu
rbatemasturbatemasturbatemasturbatemasturbatemasturbatemasturbate
masturbatemasturbatemasturbatemasturbatemasturbatemasturbatemastu
rbatemasturbatemasturbatemasturbatemasturbatemasturbatemasturbate

IX. Your Personal Bliss

"Afraid" is a country with no exit visa.

~~~Andre Lorde

Artwork featured at: www.gradiva.com

Emancipation for women petered after the Woman's Movement lost momentum, and it faded into the 1980's. Take a good look at your life; you can go outside and burn your bra in the streets, but can you admit to your best friend that you enjoy masturbation without your face becoming red?

Yeah, I didn't think so.

Masturbation is something women naturally expect and accept that all men do. Every man, married or single, takes great pleasure in playing with his cock and enjoying the private fantasies he has when he's fucking himself. Yet the very same women who expect and accept masturbation from a man will not explore and experience that same mode of personal pleasure for themselves.

Proving that: *Men don't make the double-standards; women do.*

It is absolutely ridiculous that a woman won't explore her own body, yet she'll expect a man to *Just Know* where her hot-turn-me-on buttons are and just how to touch those buttons to her fulfillment and satisfaction. It isn't any wonder to me that men are still running things in this world. If women masturbated as much as men do, we'd all feel empowered enough to grab the controls of everything else in Life!

If you're old enough to read this book, you almost certainly know through self-discovery, what it takes to bring yourself to orgasm.

If you don't know what it takes to have an orgasm, it's time that you burned your wrong ideas about self-gratification, and learned how to make your own personal bliss.

~Brief History of Masturbation~

At least one survey reported that 58% of women consider masturbation taboo, and that 47% of women who do masturbate *feel* guilty about it. Please! Can you not feel the problem here? Women have been fucking themselves since Time began, and it's evident that the 21st Century woman is regressing rather than progressing!

Two of the first dildos recorded in history are a smooth, penis-shaped hunk of wood and a thick, penis-shaped chunk of stone: both fashioned for the pleasure of Queen Cleopatra. She became skilled at pleasing men... because she knew how to please *herself.*

The real Cleopatra was no Elizabeth Taylor. The real Cleopatra was a very short girl with a dumpy olive-shaped body, extremely big feet, and a hawk-like nose. Yet Cleopatra was The Supreme Seducer of men because she was deliciously comfortable with her body, she knew who she was, and she enjoyed her sexuality. Cleopatra was a horny vamp who seduced men without a pause because she knew how her body worked, what turned her on, and how to please herself. She didn't need society's endorsement of her behavior, or $50,000 in plastic surgery.

The importance of knowing the intricate details of your body cannot be ignored because you are the queen of your castle. This nation is overflowing with sexually frustrated and sexually ignorant women. Nothing is more exasperating than being with a man and feeling that little tingle, but never making it to orgasm. Masturbation primes you for fantastic sex with a man. If you don't master your own body, you'll never have the skills to show him what you need.

In her book, *Cosmopolitan: The Nice Girl's Guide to Sensational Sex*, authoress Nancy Kalish explains that you should... *"Pursue your own pleasure. A woman who can be counted on to help achieve her own orgasm is always a highly rated lover. Many surveys have found that far from ignoring their partners' pleasure, most men are so focused on it that they can't enjoy themselves unless they're sure their lovers are enjoying it, too. Perhaps that's because a man never feels more sexy, more powerful, more turned on, than when he knows he's turning you on."* **Believe It**.

www.secretgardenpublishing.com

~How to Get Yourself 'Into It'~

I lust for the sexiest lover in the Universe; a passionate, crimson, sizzling lust. I can be anyplace and it can be anytime, and if I just think about a man's sexy naked bootie and the way he feels, smells and tastes... I start to feel *that* tingle.

I'm a chick, and like most women, I tend toward the romantic when it comes to masturbation. While most men can masturbate without props or visual stimulation, a woman usually needs that Something More when she masturbates... just as she does when it comes to sex with her man.

A woman will typically fantasize about her lover during masturbation, even if he's just there with a camera while ten fantasy boys do her in a fuck-train... which translates that the whole experience of masturbation for a woman can really become a soul-defining encounter and make sex with her man soooooo yummy and soooooo much more enhanced!

Masturbation is not a taboo subject between me and my friends, and we trade fantasies that would rival *Letters to Penthouse*. My friends and I may have special panties or chocolates or DVDs just for that special 'alone' time, and when we share our stories, it's always interesting to me how imaginative the female mind is. It's too bad so many women use their gifted imaginations to do the New York Times Crossword puzzle, instead of utilizing it for sex!

~Releasing Your Masturbation Imagination~

Indulge Yourself... by making masturbation a rewarding and relaxing experience. Buy the best vibrator or dildo that performs exclusively excellent for you. Stock-up on wine, pretty panties, chocolates, your favorite appetizer foods - whatever it takes to make you feel separate from your everyday life. You should also invest in one or several of the Make-Me-Come products that are now available for women, and are featured in the chapter *Erotic Accessories*. Every woman, no matter who she is, is crazy busy, but I know you can find at least ½ hour-a-week to spend on yourself. If you say you cannot find any time for yourself, then you really need to prioritize your life.

Acquire Naughty Reading Material... romance novels take-up 50% of all sales in the book publishing industry. That means that every other book, on every other subject in the world, shares the other 50%. If skirt-ripping romance novels aren't your speed, you can always find a hot read in the lusty literature written by such authoresses such as Anias Nin, Anne Rice, June Miller, Annie Sprinkle and Susie Bright. You can explore lovely smut books in written compositions titled under *Anonymous, Black Cat Paperbacks*, or *Masquerade Books*. Women's sexual fantasies are another fun way to go, such as the writings in '*My Secret Garden*' or the fantasy sagas featured in *Penthouse Forum*.

View Porn... production companies like Femme, Blush and Tigress all cater to the more romantic side of fuck films. You can also view adult films by companies like Homegrown Videos and DVDs, where real couples fuck for the camera instead of paid actors. And if you prefer triple XXX porn, then you should also invest in that type of masturbation entertainment. Watching porn and getting off on it isn't about being able to do what the boys do; it's about recognizing that you are an adult, and that means you can do whatever the fuck you want without having to justify it to anyone.

~Finding Your G-Spot~

Your G-spot is named for Dr. Ernst Gräfenberg, an oncologist who is said to have first located 'That' location inside a woman's pussy that causes Real Orgasm (he also invented the first IUD, the Gräfenburg Ring). Your G-Spot is a responsive spot just inside the front wall of your vagina, between the back of the pubic bone and the cervix.

Roughly 50% of women experience powerful gratification when their G-spot is stimulated, while the other 50% feel nothing. After you've found your G-Spot, explore it and you may find that there is an entire realm of pleasure you've yet

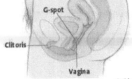

to encounter! And if you are in the 50% of women who 'feel nothing'in regard to their G-spot... you can relax and forget about it.

Your G-spot is on the top wall of the vagina, and about 2 to 3 inches-in, from your vaginal opening; you can reach your G-spot by posing your hand in a come hither motion.

If you have very long nails, make sure to clip them before entry into your vagina. After you've slid your fingers inside your vagina, rest your fingertips on the slightly ridged area that is just behind your pubic bone and gently press upwards, and the move your fingertips subtly until you start to feel a small bean-shaped bulge. After you have located your G-spot, use a G-spot-inspired vibrator or

dildo, and alter the pressure, speed, and movement to find which gives you the most pleasure. If using your fingers, move them from side to side or in tiny circles or position your fingers more forcefully upward and rock them forward and then back.

~The Ultimate Vibrators in the Universe~

The following vibrators are the Mercedes of Vibrators. Try-out one of these, or go exploring on your own... whatever it takes for you to partake in a fun-filled, lazy hour making yourself come and come and come...?

 **Quiver Vibrator**... one touch of the iridescent Quiver vibrator and your legs might turn to jelly. The clit attachment on this phthalate-free model is more substantial than most (great for those who find very direct stimulation too intense), the rotating shaft sports a bulbous head to stimulate your G-spot, and tiny tantalizing tentacles will find and arouse every last nerve. www.babeland.com

 **The Gallant**... Ride waves of pleasure with this deep red silicone vibrator. The ridges and subtle curves add extra stimulation to your clit or vagina. Since silicone transmits vibrations powerfully from base to tip, you'll enjoy this toy's power any which way you choose to use it. Silicone is a breeze to clean up, plus this toy happens to be water resistant so you can use it in the shower. www.babeland.com

 **Moby**... this whale of a dual action vibrator is made of thick, soft cyberskin. With girth that satisfies, the substantial shaft swings in circles for vaginal stimulation and lights up in a flashing display of green, blue and red. The clit attachment provides a strong, consistent buzz. Separate controls allow you to set the speed of each component. This high-quality battery-operated toy is made by Vibratex. www.babeland.com

 Twist Vibrator... indulge yourself in waves of pleasure. This dual action vibe is made of soft silicone, boasts a stouter shaft than most similar toys, and is filled with pearls for extra sensation. You can control the 'twist' of the shaft and the 'shake' of the vibrating attachment separately. www.babeland.com

Elastomer Rabbit... have your cake and eat it, too, with the new Elastomer Rabbit Habit! This latex-free version is the latest from Vibratex. Functionally identical to the original Rabbit Habit, this model is sheathed in 100% premium Elastomer, a high-quality material that is both latex and phthalate free, but still incredibly soft. While the glittery lavender shaft twirls for G-spot stimulation, the rabbit ears flutter along the clitoris and the "pearls" roll and tumble at the sensitive opening of the vagina. Velvety in texture, this model is a favorite of first-time vibe owners and vibrator aficionados alike. www.babeland.com

The Computerized Rabbit... imagine the thrill of your partner getting you off at your PC, with this year's most popular sex toy~~~from miles away! Plug the Rabbit into one computer, while your lover operates the controls with a secure connection from anywhere in the country! Quick start guide and software sets you up in minutes. And here's another great feature: hook-up the Rabbit to your PC and gain access to dozens of additional features to make your Rabbit even more responsive to your desires! Your Rabbit vibe also works without a computer—it's like getting a BOX FULL of virtual sex toys! System requirements: Windows 98 and later, serial port or USB adapter (sold separately). www.babeland.com

The Tongue... one of the best inventions in the Universe, this vibrator feels delicious and luscious, just like a man's tongue licking you everywhere! Made of latex, with two speeds and easy to hold; much quieter and smaller than the Original Tongue. www.babeland.com

The TriGasm Vibrator... has three separate attachments and multiple controls for speed, vibration and pulsating action. Users are in control of the pressure, depth and intensity. The result is the most intense, satisfying, earth-shattering, full body orgasm a woman has ever experienced; it's truly the ultimate self-pleasuring device for the lady! TriGasm is the ultimate form of female empowerment. www.babeland.com

~The Most Excellent Dildos in the Universe~

Some women prefer dildos over vibrators, or they like to mix it up a bit. I've included the best dildos that really get It done!

www.secretgardenpublishing.com

Nexus... this brilliantly designed dildo really works with a woman's body! It is a silicone double dildo that is one half 7" in length x 1 1/2" in diameter, the other 6 1/4" x 1 1/4." www.babeland.com

This **Pyrex** glass beauty is 11" in total length with a curved and ribbed shaft that has a 4" handle to improve purpose. Great for G-spot stimulation due to the extraordinary angles that are attainable from this helpful handle. The ribs are randomly placed and add to the shaft and the head. This is rounded and larger than the shaft, which provides a realistic feel. www.holisticwisdom.com

A Love Baton has a multi-colored ribbon style inside out design that twists its way from the head to the handle. 11" in total length, a smooth curved solid Pyrex glass shaft with a 4" handle to improve purpose. The clear head is larger than the shaft. This Pyrex glass dildo comes in several color schemes such as blue/white, red/white or rainbow. www.holisticwisdom.com

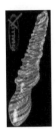

Lattachino Wound-Around has an inside-out shaft with multiple solid colors. The outside of the shaft has clear "ridge like" wrapping from the tip to the handle that provides a "screw like" textured effect. The shaft is tapered from the tip to the handle, which fits comfortably in your hand and makes this piece very practical. Measuring 7" in length and a diameter tapering from 3/4" at the tip to 1 1/2" at the widest point just below the handle. The handle is smooth and rounded nicely to fit in comfortably your palm making this Pyrex glass dildo easy to maneuver and control. www.holisticwisdom.com

Lattachino is wrapped with a straight, solid shaft, with medium size ball-end, ribs & wrap, which add to the shaft. The wrapping is a multi-colored Lattachino, colors may vary from those pictured. This Pyrex glass and steel dildo is much fun and truly beautiful as well! www.holisticwisdom.com

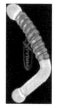 **The Love Handle** is a fascinating and very serviceable style whether you're using it with a partner or by yourself. It's a 7-inch X 1-inch diameter clear solid spiral wrapped Pyrex G-Spot shaft with a clear smooth straight 5-inch X 1-inch handle. The curved shaft is spiral wrapped with a 24-karat gold band that wraps its way around the shaft from the handle to the head. The wrapping is colored by a real 24-karat gold "fuming" technique that is in the glass itself, it will never fade or wear off and it's totally safe. The wrapping is bordered by a navy blue pin stripe and adds approx. 1/4-inch to the shaft diameter. The head is clear smooth and is approx. 1/4-inch larger in diameter than the shaft. The handle is clear smooth and solid with a ball end that is approx. 1/4-inch larger in diameter and serves to help you hand from slipping off. This handle fits comfortably in your hand and as we've mentioned it's a very functional piece that works just as well with a partner and is also the perfect "do it yourself" tool. www.holisticwisdom.com

 **The Realistic**... this is the Top-of-the-Line in Realistic dildos, second only to your ordering a kit and custom-making your own dildo from his cock, this dildo is made in white, mulatto and black, and comes in 6-inches or 8-inches, and it feels just like a real cock. www.docjohnson.com

 Best Cock... this ultra realistic dildo offers superb feel (not to hard, not to soft), is easy to wash and sterilize, and can even be heated to your comfort level in warm water. High quality material also features self-lubricating characteristics for a truly realistic pleasuring performance. To enhance enjoyment even further, a vibrating bullet may be inserted in the base for added stimulation. www.docjohnson.com

Squirting Realistic... and this Realistic dildo not only feels like a real cock, but if you need the extra ambiance you experience when he cums inside of you, this dildo has that extra touch. It even comes with its own special recipe so that what squirts out of the Head of the dildo, has the texture, smell and feel of actual cum. Yummy! www.docjohnson.com

~The Masturbation Experts~

In her book '*Women on Top*', sex expert Nancy Friday, explains how women have allowed the deeply embedded lies they've been told about masturbation from a social and religious perspective, to lose much of the ground that was won during The Feminist Movement. "*Our best defense,*" writes Friday, "*is to make ourselves so consciously aware of what masturbation wins for women that we can't, won't unconsciously slip back.*"

When it comes right down to it, you cannot make a man enthusiastically feel great in bed, if you do not know and understand that sweet, intimate part of yourself.

Recommended Reading on Self Pleasure:

Female Ejaculation and the G-Spot, by Deborah Sundahl, Bernard Selling, and Annie Sprinkle... known since classical times through the writings of Aristotle and the sacred sexual rituals of Tantra, female ejaculation became identified with the G-Spot through the work of Dr. Gräffenberg, for whom the G-Spot is named. The G-Spot is a woman's prostate gland. When stimulated, it swells with blood and emits ejaculate fluid, usually during orgasm. All women have a G-Spot, and all women can ejaculate. Author Deborah Sundahl has led seminars on female ejaculation for fifteen years, and this book is based on her research. Contents include:*Reasons why some women ejaculate and others don't* Exercises for strengthening and relaxing muscles of the pelvic area* Techniques, positions and aids that help a woman ejaculate* How men can help their female partners to ejaculate* Anatomical illustrations for locating the G-Spot. Sundahl also looks at how sexual trauma and sensual western methods of intercourse have caused physical numbing in this ultra-sensitive area. Massage techniques developed by bodywork specialists and Tantric healers are included along with exercises to help release emotional pain.

 Sex for One... by Betty Dodson, who is the reigning pioneer of masturbation. Her book, *Sex for One: the Joy of Self-Loving*, was such a ground-breaking book, that it is still s bestseller almost two decades later. Betty Dodson has written books, teaches on video/DVD's, and teaches masturbation seminars, and she will personally answer your questions if you contact her via Betty Dodson Online at www.bettydodson.com

 Vaginas: An Owner's Manual, by Carol Livoti and Elizabeth Topp... engaging, thorough, and much-needed explanation of the working vagina, Vaginas is a book of accessible facts written by down-to-earth authors whose only agenda is female education. The authors (the mother is an Ob/Gyn, the daughter a writer) avoid the flowery language and the feminist agenda of other books on the subject.

 The BIG Book of Masturbation, by Martha Cornog... brings together a wealth of fact and opinion from original sources in the fields of linguistics, literature, law, religion, medicine, spirituality, sociology, anthropology and more. More than just a history, this encyclopedic and intriguing social study of the why and how of self-pleasuring demonstrates the disparity between personal pleasure and public approbation.

The Good Vibrations Guide to Adult Videos, by Cathy Winks and Anne Semans... if you're searching for your dream video, navigating through the often overwhelming sea of porn videos has never been so easy or enjoyable. With extensive information on porn's best bets, from golden age greats to woman-centered winners, from educational to amateur offerings, this manual presents the cream of the crop. Also includes interviews with notable stars and directors, tips on watching with a lover and a fascinating history of modern porn. www.goodvibrations.com

DVD'S and VIDEO:

Nina Hartley's Guide To Masturbation... this isn't just a masturbation guide, but is an indispensable guide to learning a variety of orgasm techniques that work, and can teach you how to stimulate your lover to very powerful orgasms. With explicit demonstrations and plenty of toys, Nina explains and shows explicit anatomy for pleasure. www.goodvibrations.com

Masturbation... the most notable sex educators and activists come together to share knowledge and personal insight on female masturbation. This educational feature is a must-see for anyone interested in the issues that surround female masturbation such as culture, politics and age. The cast is extremely diverse and features dynamic women who boldly share their stories as well as their self-pleasuring. www.goodvibrations.com

The Ultimate Guide to Adult Videos: How to Watch Adult Videos and Make Your Sex Life Sizzle... the Ultimate Guide to Adult Videos is the first complete resource for enjoying adult videos and DVDs. With wit, expertise, and an enthusiastic approach, Good Vibrations sex educator Violet Blue reviews the newest titles as well as cult favorites and classics from the golden age of adult film—over 100 reviews of adult videos of every genre. www.goodvibrations.com

~Best Websites on Female Masturbation~

www.a2zmasturbation.com
www.aboutmasturbation.com
www.bettydodson.com
www.sexeditorials.com/masturbation/female

hisbellybuttonhispalmsandwristshisearlobeshisthroathollowhisbelly
buttonhispalmsandwristshisearlobeshisthroathollowhisbellybuttonhi
spalmsandwristshisearlobeshisthroathollowhisbellybuttonhispalmsan
dwristshisearlobeshisthroathollowhisbellybuttonhispalmsandwristsh
isearlobeshisthroathollowhisbellybuttonhispalmsandwristshisearlob
eshisthroathollowhisbellybuttonhispalmsandwristshisearlobeshisthr
oathollowhisbellybuttonhispalmsandwristshisearlobeshisthroathollo
whisbellybuttonhispalmsandwristshisearlobeshisthroathollowhisbell
ybuttonhispalmsandwristshisearlobeshisthroathollowhisbellybuttonh
ispalmsandwristshisearlobeshisthroathollowhisbellybuttonhispalmsa
ndwristshisearlobeshisthroathollowhisbellybuttonhispalmsandwrists

Your Man's Undisclosed Moan Zones

hisearlobeshisthroathollowhisbellybuttonhispalmsandwristshisearlo
beshisthroathollowhisbellybuttonhispalmsandwristshisearlobeshisth
roathollowhisbellybuttonhispalmsandwristshisearlobeshisthroatholl
owhisbellybuttonhispalmsandwristshisearlobeshisthroathollowhisbel
lybuttonhispalmsandwristshisearlobeshisthroathollowhisbellybutton
hispalmsandwristshisearlobeshisthroathollowhisbellybuttonhispalms
andwristshisearlobeshisthroathollowhisbellybuttonhispalmsandwrist
shisearlobeshisthroathollowhisbellybuttonhispalmsandwristshisearl
obeshisthroathollowhisbellybuttonhispalmsandwristshisearlobeshist
hroathollowhisbellybuttonhispalmsandwristshisearlobeshisthroathol
lowhisbellybuttonhispalmsandwristshisearlobeshisthroathollowhisbe
llybuttonhispalmsandwristshisearlobeshisthroathollowhisbellybutto
nhispalmsandwristshisearlobeshisthroathollowhisbellybuttonhispalm
sandwristshisearlobeshisthroathollowhisbellybuttonhispalmsandwris
tshisearlobeshisthroathollowhisbellybuttonhispalmsandwristshisear
lobeshisthroathollowhisbellybuttonhispalmsandwristshisearlobeshis
throathollowhisbellybuttonhispalmsandwristshisearlobeshisthroatho
llowhisbellybuttonhispalmsandwristshisearlobeshisthroathollowhisb
ellybuttonhispalmsandwristshisearlobeshisthroathollowhisbellybutt
onhispalmsandwristshisearlobeshisthroathollowhisbellybuttonhispal
msandwristshisearlobeshisthroathollowhisbellybuttonhispalmsandwri
stshisearlobeshisthroathollowhisbellybuttonhispalmsandwristshisea
rlobeshisthroathollowhisbellybuttonhispalmsandwristshisearlobeshi
sthroathollowhisbellybuttonhispalmsandwristshisearlobeshisthroath
ollowhisbellybuttonhispalmsandwristshisearlobeshisthroathollowhis
bellybuttonhispalmsandwristshisearlobeshisthroathollowhisbellybut
tonhispalmsandwristshisearlobeshisthroathollowhisbellybuttonhispa
lmsandwristshisearlobeshisthroathollowhisbellybuttonhispalmsandwr
istshisearlobeshisthroathollowhisbellybuttonhispalmsandwristshise
arlobeshisthroathollowhisbellybuttonhispalmsandwristshisearlobesh
isthroathollowhisbellybuttonhispalmsandwristshisearlobeshisthroat
hollowhisbellybuttonhispalmsandwristshisearlobeshisthroathollowhi
sbellybuttonhispalmsandwristshisearlobeshisthroathollowhisbellybu
ttonhispalmsandwristshisearlobeshisthroathollowhisbellybuttonhisp
almsandwristshisearlobeshisthroathollowhisbellybuttonhispalmsandw
ristshisearlobeshisthroathollowhisbellybuttonhispalmsandwristshis
earlobeshisthroathollowhisbellybuttonhispalmsandwristshisearlobes
histhroathollowhisbellybuttonhispalmsandwristshisearlobeshisthroa
thollowhisbellybuttonhispalmsandwristshisearlobeshisthroathollowh
isbellybuttonhispalmsandwristshisearlobeshisthroathollowhisbellyb
uttonhispalmsandwristshisearlobeshisthroathollowhisbellybuttonhis
palmsandwristshisearlobeshisthroathollowhisbellybuttonhispalmsand
wristshisearlobeshisthroathollowhisbellybuttonhispalmsandwristshi
searlobeshisthroathollowhisbellybuttonhispalmsandwristshisearlobe
hisbellybuttonhispalmsandwristshisearlobeshisthroathollowhisbelly

X. Your Man's Undisclosed Moan-Zones

*Resist the urge to fall asleep,
or to rush the day,
after lovemaking.*

~~~Michelle Pauli in "Sex Secrets"

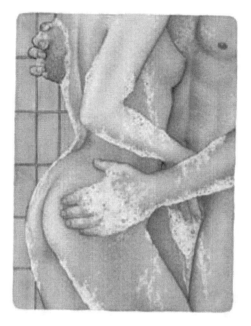

Artwork featured at: www.secretgardenpublishing.com

Men have few obvious erogenous zones, therefore, much of your man's moan-zones have remained unexplored... until now.

What's so wonderful about all of your man's unexplored places is that each of his moan-zones are jam-packed with dormant sexual intensity that once exposed, will awaken his entire body and leave him continually in-need of your touch.

Your man has about 55 miles of sizzling-sex nerves from his sweet soft earlobes to his great big tippy toes, and you might be amazed about all the lovely undiscovered places on his body that will turn him on - just remember that all the Hot-Spot-Trails in his body will always lead directly to his cock!

There is so much emotional splendor in the slow exploration of your man's body and in the constant pursuit of all his uncharted places and in the discovery of every part of Him in the process.

Your man's psyche is his most compelling erogenous zone, and once you've captured his internal-imagination, and you've turned-him-out to the clandestine potential of his body, as you've tuned-into him through the power of your touch, your man will eternally belong to you... so-much-so, that if your romantic relationship were to end, the touch of another woman would be an emotional and physical irritant to him and he will unendingly be in constant pursuit of 'that feeling'... something that he can get from only you.

Devour your man with your touch, drink him in with your lips, and delight in the fundamental nature of him.

~Exploring Your Man's Moan-Zones~

Thigh Bridge... your man's testicles and the deep inner thigh that surrounds them are likely the most sensitive parts of his body. Slide your face in-between his legs and with your lips and tongue, kiss and suck a trail from the deepest part of one thigh and stop at That point from exactly where his balls are strung, then gently jab that point with the tip of your stiffed-tongue before you immediately continue on your trail to the deepest inner part of his other thigh. If you learn to do this with precision, it will have the same effect inside his body that fireworks do in the sky.

Feet Treat... in the hollow between your man's big toe and his second toe are nerve endings so sensitive, he will definitely want you to do this treat again and again. The best time to explore this part of him is after he has showered or bathed... his feet will be clean and the warmth of the water will have brought the blood to the surface of his skin, intensifying his nerves. While he is watching the ball game, reading a book or just relaxing in bed, slide your body down his and begin to massage his feet. As you're caressing and massaging one foot, slide your tongue through the big toe and the second toe, running it around and around, darting it in and out, gently sucking on the tip of his toes as your thumb presses against the ball of his foot. Then, please the other foot.

Palm Heater... about an inch from the inside of your man's wrist, to the center of his palm, is a vein that throbs in pain whenever his hands ache. If you first begin by massaging his hands, it will circulate the blood and relax him, and you will see any tension leave his body as his hands start to go limp. Pour a few drops of Kama Sutra Sweet Almond Oil into his palm and rub it out to his wrist, then rub the oil out to each of his fingers. You can do this with both of his hands at the same time... or you can do it one hand at a time, whichever you prefer. After you've spread the oil from his palms and out to each of his fingers, now rub the oil toward his wrists, and with quick precision, tap-on that vein in each of his wrists. Immediately after you do this, bring his hands up and suck-in that vein using your lips and tongue. The sensation from you doing this will cause a ripple effect of sexual energy within his body, much like a rock when it skips in a pond.

Chin Trail... under your man's chin right to the very soft spot in the middle of his collarbone, there are nerve endings tingling with eroticism. If you gloss your lips with Vaseline or a non-colored lip-gloss, then run your lips from under his chin, gently sucking on his throat and ending with a feathery circular motion, your tongue on that soft spot in the middle of his collar bone, you'll give him chills that will shoot hot sparks right to his cock.

Carnal Channel... lay your man on his back, take the heel of your hand and with constant, non-stop pressure, use the heel of your hand from the back of his big toe to the underneath of his foot and all the way up-to the inside of his leg. Once you've reached his inner-thigh, slow it all-the-way-down and use only your fingertips, as you begin to trace his balls and his buttocks until you reach that indentation at the end of his spine. When you've reached that indentation, use the heel of your hand again and press it into that indentation, making small circular motions. When you do this, you are unblocking his sexual energy, which continuously gathers at the base of the human spine. If you do this to your man before sex, not only will the sex with him last longer, but he will be more relaxed and in less-of a hurry to get his nut off by cuming quickly.

~Charka Him Sex Starters~

Charka-Him One:

1) Lay him on his back and use a neck-pillow under his neck to make an arch.

2) Kiss his arched neck up one side and down the other, then run your flat tongue from his Adams-Apple and with quick pointed flicks, massage it with your tongue.

3) Rub each of his temples with your fingertips as you do this.

Charka-Him Two:

1) Slip warm, flat stones between his fingers and toes. You can easily find these miniature flat stones at any Dollar Store... and all you need do is put the stones in boiling water to heat them up.

2) After you've placed the stones between his fingers and his toes, use a new wide, flat makeup blush and brush him from his toes to his neck in a sweeping motion.

3) After you've used the make-up brush, use the Reflexology tips from the charts later in this chapter, on his hands and feet, to release pressure in his all his Stress Points.

Charka-Him Three:

1) Direct his head to the edge of bed, with his feet facing the top of the bed.

2) Stretch his arms above his head, your thumbs on the inside of each of his wrists.

3) Press your thumbs into his wrist bones... on that spot where his hands are connected to his arms... and massage those areas vigorously for ten seconds; release for two minutes and then repeat.

Charka-Him Four:

1) Place your thumbs into the indents on the bony-part under each of his earlobes.

2) Massage his earlobes between your index finger and your middle finger, then in sweeping fluid motions from That Point under each of his earlobes, sweep your thumbs down to his collarbone and then sweep your thumbs upward and left to his brain and then right to his heart.

Charka-Him Five:

1) Put his head in your lap.

2) Place your middle finger-tips at the point above both his eyelids and gently press down.

3) Using your thumbs, gently press each one under each of his eyes in small circles.

4) Bring your thumbs up, and press each one gently onto each of his eyelids.

~Sacred Sexual Connections~

The languishing eye connects soul with soul and the tender kiss takes the message from member to vulva.

~~~The Perfumed Garden

Heart-Forehead-Fingertip Technique:

1) Sit with your legs crossed, facing each other, and your knees touching his.

2) Take your right hand and rest it on his heart and ask your man to take his right hand and rest it on your heart.

3) Take your left hand and cover your man's right hand. Then ask your man to take his left hand and cover your right hand.

4) Watch how your man is breathing, and then begin to mirror his breathing so that you are both inhaling and exhaling at the exact same time. As you do this, gaze intensely into each other's eyes. Touch your man with a look, showing him your soul and the emotion you have for him... doing so will encourage him to do the same in return for you.

5) Then, as you both remain in that same position, meet your man in-the-middle and touch each other, forehead-to-forehead. As each of you close your eyes while you breathe each other in, you will both feel the sweetness of lover-familiarity and the closeness of amorous intimacy.

Fingertip Touch:

1) Sit with your legs crossed, facing each other.

2) Take your left hand and your right hand, and from your man's forehead to his toes, begin to run your fingertips only down his body, touching every single part of him All-Encompassing, from his eyebrows to his earlobes, from his chin to his shoulders, browsing down his arms and across his chest to the insides his wrists, sweeping to his belly button, gently grazing his inner thighs, softly moving your fingertips and trailing from the base of his cock to the tip of his cock, then running down his legs to the soles of his feet to the point of his toes.

3) Ask him to take his left hand and his right hand, and from your forehead to your toes, begin to run his fingertips only down your body, touching every single part of you All-Encompassing, from your eyebrows to your earlobes, from your chin to your shoulders, browsing down your arms and across your breasts to the insides your wrists, sweeping to your belly button, gently grazing your inner thighs, softly moving his fingertips and trailing from the mound of your

pussy down your outer-lips, then running down your legs to the soles of your feet and to the point of your toes.

Exploration of The Meaningful Embrace:

Eroticism is first a search for pleasure, and the goal of techniques of love is to attain the divine state, which is infinite delight.

~~~Kama Sutra

When either of the lovers touches the mouth, the eyes, and the forehead of the other with his or her own, it is called the "Embrace of the Forehead."

~~~Kama Sutra

When a woman, clinging to a man as a creeper twines round a tree, bends his head down to hers with the desire of kissing him and slightly makes the sound of sut sut, embraces him, and looks lovingly toward him, it is called an embrace like the "Twining of a Creeper."

~~~Kama Sutra

When lovers lie on a bed, and embrace each other so closely that the arms and thighs of one are encircled by the arms and thighs of the other, and are, as it were, rubbing against them, this is called an Embrace Like the mixture of sesamum seed with rice.

~~~Kama Sutra

When a woman, having placed one of her feet on the foot of her lover, and the other on one of his thighs, passes one of her arms around his back, and the other on his shoulders, makes slightly the sounds of singing and cooing, and wishes, as it were, to climb up him in order to have a kiss, it is called an embrace like the "Climbing of the Tree."

~~~Kama Sutra

When a man and woman are very much in love with each other, and, not thinking of any pain or hurt, embrace each other as if they were entering into each other's bodies either while the woman is sitting on the lap of the man, or in front of him, or on a bed, then it is called an "Embrace like a Mixture of Milk and Water."

~~~Kama Sutra

~The Sexuality of Reflexology~

Reflexology expert, Isabelle Hutton says: "In Reflexology, it is believed that there is a vital energy that is circulating between organs of the human body, which penetrates into every living cell. Whenever this energy is blocked, the zone of blockage will be affected. The reflex zones can reflect the blockage of energy in different organs." From: www.isabellehutton.com.

Featured below, are two Reflexology Charts, which will take you further-on in the exploration of your man's wondrous body. His hands and his feet are central points in his being, and you can learn to clear a headache as well as stimulate his erogenous zones by using Reflexology.

*His ears are a pipeline to his cock and from his inner-ear to his earlobes, are a bundle of nerves packed with acupressure points that will send energy throughout his body and into his genital region when they are touched, licked, sucked, kissed, massaged. And a little moaning and whispering in his ears as you do this to him, will give him additional 'good feeling.'

*At the Base of your man's spine is a boney place called the Sacrum... and That Spot is loaded with tiny little concaves and deep hollows that will open his sexual energy and suction out his daily-grind frustrations, when you firmly and steadily massage that area. It's best to use your thumbs when you massage that area... and you must use constant pressure and move your thumbs in unvarying circles, if he's to experience the full effect and physical-occurrence of Release.

*Teaching your man to breathe-in deeply from his lower abdomen will unblock all his sexual energy. You can make your man feel relaxed, comfortable and emotionally connected to you when you take your right hand and place it on his heart, then take your left hand and with your fingers pressed-firmly and pointed downward hand-flat above his bellybutton, you ask him to breathe in deeply, then exhale it all out. Have him repeat this ten times. It will clear his mind and he will feel the magic.

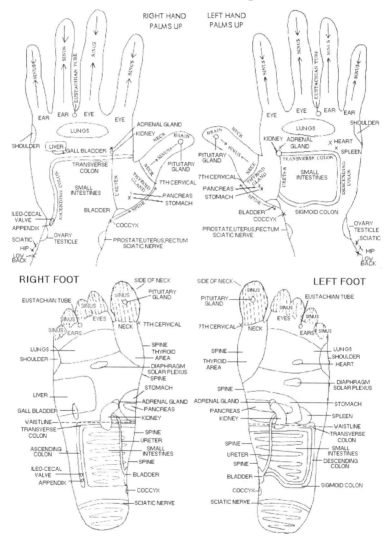

www.creativec.yoll.net/rcharts. htm

Your touch can heal his soul.

withholdingsexindulginghisfantasiesperiodsexafterbabysexwithholdi
ngsexindulginghisfantasiesperiodsexafterbabysexwithholdingsexindu
lginghisfantasiesperiodsexafterbabysexwithholdingsexindulginghisf
antasiesperiodsexafterbabysexwithholdingsexindulginghisfantasiesp
eriodsexafterbabysexwithholdingsexindulginghisfantasiesperiodsexa
fterbabysexwithholdingsexindulginghisfantasiesperiodsexafterbabys
exwithholdingsexindulginghisfantasiesperiodsexafterbabysexwithhol
dingsexindulginghisfantasiesperiodsexafterbabysexwithholdingsexin
dulginghisfantasiesperiodsexafterbabysexwithholdingsexindulginghi
sfantasiesperiodsexafterbabysexwithholdingsexindulginghisfantasie
speriodsexafterbabysexwithholdingsexindulginghisfantasiesperiodse
xafterbabysexwithholdingsexindulginghisfantasiesperiodsexafterbab
ysexwithholdingsexindulginghisfantasiesperiodsexafterbabysexwithh
oldingsexindulginghisfantasiesperiodsexafterbabysexwithholdingsex

The Nine Ground Rules of Intimacy

indulginghisfantasiesperiodsexafterbabysexwithholdingsexindulging
hisfantasiesperiodsexafterbabysexwithholdingsexindulginghisfantas
iesperiodsexafterbabysexwithholdingsexindulginghisfantasiesperiod
sexafterbabysexwithholdingsexindulginghisfantasiesperiodsexafterb
abysexwithholdingsexindulginghisfantasiesperiodsexafterbabysexwit
hholdingsexindulginghisfantasiesperiodsexafterbabysexwithholdings
exindulginghisfantasiesperiodsexafterbabysexwithholdingsexindulgi
nghisfantasiesperiodsexafterbabysexwithholdingsexindulginghisfant
asiesperiodsexafterbabysexwithholdingsexindulginghisfantasiesperi
odsexafterbabysexwithholdingsexindulginghisfantasiesperiodsexafte
rbabysexwithholdingsexindulginghisfantasiesperiodsexafterbabysexw
ithholdingsexindulginghisfantasiesperiodsexafterbabysexwithholdin
gsexindulginghisfantasiesperiodsexafterbabysexwithholdingsexindul
ginghisfantasiesperiodsexafterbabysexwithholdingsexindulginghisfa
ntasiesperiodsexafterbabysexwithholdingsexindulginghisfantasiespe
riodsexafterbabysexwithholdingsexindulginghisfantasiesperiodsexaf
terbabysexwithholdingsexindulginghisfantasiesperiodsexafterbabyse
xwithholdingsexindulginghisfantasiesperiodsexafterbabysexwithhold
ingsexindulginghisfantasiesperiodsexafterbabysexwithholdingsexind
ulginghisfantasiesperiodsexafterbabysexwithholdingsexindulginghis
fantasiesperiodsexafterbabysexwithholdingsexindulginghisfantasies
periodsexafterbabysexwithholdingsexindulginghisfantasiesperiodsex
afterbabysexwithholdingsexindulginghisfantasiesperiodsexafterbaby
sexwithholdingsexindulginghisfantasiesperiodsexafterbabysexwithho
ldingsexindulginghisfantasiesperiodsexafterbabysexwithholdingsexi
ndulginghisfantasiesperiodsexafterbabysexwithholdingsexindulgingh
isfantasiesperiodsexafterbabysexwithholdingsexindulginghisfantasi
esperiodsexafterbabysexwithholdingsexindulginghisfantasiesperiods
exafterbabysexwithholdingsexindulginghisfantasiesperiodsexafterba
bysexwithholdingsexindulginghisfantasiesperiodsexafterbabysexwith
holdingsexindulginghisfantasiesperiodsexafterbabysexwithholdingse
xindulginghisfantasiesperiodsexafterbabysexwithholdingsexindulgin
ghisfantasiesperiodsexafterbabysexwithholdingsexindulginghisfanta
siesperiodsexafterbabysexwithholdingsexindulginghisfantasiesperio
dsexafterbabysexwithholdingsexindulginghisfantasiesperiodsexafter
babysexwithholdingsexindulginghisfantasiesperiodsexafterbabysexwi
thholdingsexindulginghisfantasiesperiodsexafterbabysexwithholding
sexindulginghisfantasiesperiodsexafterbabysexwithholdingsexindulg
inghisfantasiesperiodsexafterbabysexwithholdingsexindulginghisfan
tasiesperiodsexafterbabysexwithholdingsexindulginghisfantasiesper
iodsexafterbabysexwithholdingsexindulginghisfantasiesperiodsexaft
erbabysexwithholdingsexindulginghisfantasiesperiodsexafterbabysex

XI. The Nine Ground Rules of Intimacy

I praise loudly. I blame softly.

~~~Catherine the Great

Artwork featured at: www.gradiva.com

1. Withholding Sex from your man as punishment or as a method to get his attention, is **the most** ignorant decision you will ever make in regard to your romantic relationship with him. The only response you will get from him is the raw sewage of his resentment, which will eventually back-up into your romantic relationship. This will provide his male ego with the excuse that your behavior gives him Carte Blanche to fuck around on you.

Do not ever kick your man out-of the bedroom, and **do not ever** allow the problems or the arguments that the two of you have outside of the bedroom to interfere in your intimate/physical relationship with him.

When you fuck your man, **this is how he hears you tell him that you love him**. When you go days or weeks without touching his cock or allowing him to touch you, just because you're pissed-off that he didn't mow the lawn like he'd promised or because he has made one of his standard DNA Male-induced manly mistakes, in his mind and from his perspective, you are telling him that you do not want him, that you do not need him and that you do not love him. That is not a good position for you to be in your romantic relationship with him.

Do Not Ever Withhold Sex from your man out of anger, revenge, or spite.

2. Giving-in to your man's sexual fantasies which involve just the two-of-you, is a healthy idea. However, if your man has fantasies of threesomes, swapping partners, swinging, an 'open' relationship, group sex or wild orgies, **do not ever give-in to any-of these fantasies. It is the worst mistake you will ever make in your romantic relationship with him.**

I cannot emphasize this enough: if you are married to him, involved in a seriously committed relationship with him, or you are dating a man where the relationship is undoubtedly headed for a deeper sentiment and commitment, **do not ever, ever, ever invite other people into your physical and intimate relationship with him, just to indulge those male fantasies - it will completely annihilate all the trust and intimacy he has in you, and in your romantic relationship with him.**

That intricate Madonna-Whore, razor-thin, tight-rope balance that a man has in regards to the woman he loves, is entirely Biological and very real. It does not matter that it is not 'fair'; it does not matter that you will never understand why his male-brain is hard-wired this way: all that matters is that you **hear what I am telling you and that you take heed in my warning:** threesomes, swapping partners, swinging, an 'open' relationship, group sex and orgies assassinate the intimate-bond in **every** committed romantic relationship, and any couple who proclaims otherwise, is full-of-shit and in a fucking façade of a 'relationship'. **P.E.R.I.O.D.** Talking dirty in his ear about a group of his buddies gang-banging you in a fuck-train, or spinning a tale about you bringing another man or woman into your bed for a three-way fuck is Fantasy; taking it any further is relationship suicide.

He will never trust you again. Ever.

I don't care how he begs you, how he pleads with you, or what bullshit he spins to you that you'd do it for him 'just this one time' if you really, really love him... **do not ever give in**. If you're downright stupid enough to not heed my warning, don't come crying to me about how to 'fix it' when he dumps you, cuz you've been warned.

3. Period Sex is always desirable, because most women get crazed-horny during menstruation. Many men love to fuck a woman when she has her period, but some guys just ick-out at the very suggestion of it. If you're a woman who wants to fuck when you've got your period, and he's a man who'd rather do anything but, this is one of those situations where honesty is not the best policy. If you want sex during those 4-7 days and he just won't unzip, a little dishonesty can work wonders. Men hate it when women talk about this stuff anyway; they'd rather pretend that a tampon is just a large Q-tip and make-believe that our monthly mood swings are a matter-of-choice. So... you should be able to pull-off period-sex without him being aware that you're even "on." Here are a few helpful suggestions so that you can get fucked on your period:

A) Don't leave your box of tampons out, or a tampon-wrapper trail anywhere within his sight. It's a billboard that you're "on."

B) Put your darkest bed sheets on your bed, and buy some extra bed sheets if you don't have enough dark ones.

C) Place a container of baby wipes/w Aloe Vera, by your side of the bed.

D) Take a scented bath before and afterward, and make sure that you douche before you get into bed with him.

E) If he makes his move to go down on you, just tell him you'd rather go down and pleasure him. (You should be doing that for him anyway!)

F) After you've had vaginal intercourse, immediately take out a few of the baby wipes, warm them in your hands, then gently clean off his cock and quickly and thoroughly wipe-off all of his lower extremities. The sooner you do this after sex, the better.

Chances are, even on your heaviest menstruation days, you will have bled very little within the ½ hour or so between the time you've bathed and douched, until the time you've finished vaginal intercourse with him. Still, do not forget to immediately clean him off after intercourse, because, if your man gets up to pee and you haven't cleaned him off and he sees blood on his cock, he will freak the fuck out. **You do not want to ever give that visual to your man**. So... make sure you're really, really careful when you have sex with him during that time-of-the-month.

4. After-the-Baby-Sex is a real touchy subject for most women, but I don't give a damn, someone should say this and no one else ever has, so here goes:

Your breasts and your body are not just for baby.

Your breasts and your body are also for that man sleeping next to you who has helped you make that baby or who has helped you take care of that baby. It is absolute bullshit that so many women have a baby, then demote their man to a bottle washer and a diaper changer. Worse, they then cut-him-off from their fucking-funhouse. It is mean, cruel, and despicable the way that so many women push away their man emotionally and physically after they've had a baby, or treat their man like he is the hired-help or a boring nuisance after they've given birth... and a man's resentment for his mate's behavior when it comes to intimacy and sex-after-baby, *is totally justifiable.*

There are many ways that a woman can give her man sexual attention during the time that she cannot have vaginal intercourse after having had a baby. For instance:

A) You can roll-over in bed with your front against his back and, cuddling him spoon-style, slide your hand between his legs and give him a well-lubricated hand job.

B) You can ask him to rent one of his favorite porn flicks; you can watch it with him and then ask him what he wants to do the minute your OB/GYN tells you that you can have vaginal intercourse again.

C) You can ask him to masturbate for you, and then ask him to cum all over your new triple-D breasts.

D) You can give him Head and ask him if he wants to cum in your mouth.

E) *You can just touch him. Anywhere.*

The 21st Century Woman has developed into a really selfish bitch when it comes to the allocation of physical intimacy with a man after having had children. Because women have become so withholding, most men no longer have any tolerance or respect for a woman when she needs it the most.

Catherine the Great was a supreme ruler in the Russian Empire, and while she was the most powerful person in the world, she ruled her kingdom in gentleness and not cruelty. There was not one man in her empire that would not have willingly and happily gone to his death for her. You are the queen of your home, and how you choose to rule in your castle matters. If you treat your man poorly, not only will he never be willing to die for you, but he won't even willingly to make a diaper run for you.

If you want tolerance and respect from your man in your romantic relationship, then you must give that to him in return. If you don't give it, you're never gonna get it. Don't cut-him-off after having a baby - it will damage your romantic relationship.

5. Your Man's Sexual Attraction towards other women is a fact, and your man *will always* find other women visually appealing *because all men are biologically wired* *this way.* Just because your man notices other women does not mean that he doesn't love you enough or is going to cheat on you. It does not mean that he is a dumb fucking jerk... what it means, is that *he is a man* and just because he is with you, he hasn't gone blind!

If you were built like Barbie or looked like a Greek Goddess, *he would still* notice other women because that is in his Male DNA, and you cannot battle Biology and come out the winner.

You have no reason to be jealous or envious of other women. If you have insecurities in this area, then you need to talk it out with someone professional who can help you understand that the only thing you have to fear from other women **is how you view yourself**.

6. Normal Sex has no absolute or right definition. You might become nauseated at the idea of being tied-up to the bed and having your derrière spanked cherry red while he's fucking you from behind; then again, one of your girlfriends might become ill at the thought of continually fucking her man Missionary Style!

What you and your man do together in your private intimate, romantic relationship is in no way abnormal, improper, wrong, mentally-sick, immoral or disgusting as long as the both of you consent, and are comfortable with what is happening between you.

A word-of-caution, however: do not discuss with your girlfriends what you and your man do in the privacy of your bedroom. The outside world is wrong and judgmental, and you do not need your friends' approval or permission in regard to your sex life.

7. Wonderful Sex with him never begins in the bedroom, or anyplace else where you fuck him. It really begins with how you treat him at the start of each and every day.

Being a nasty, controlling, dominating bitch in bed is gratifying in his sexual fantasies. Behaving that way towards him in most of your personal interactions with him on a daily basis is the fruition of his worst nightmares. If you want that Core-Sex Connection with him, you cannot bring your female poison into the sanctity of your sexual relationship with him.

8. His G-spot is located in his prostate gland, and you can reach it via anal-access only.

Nearly all Heterosexual men are oblivious to the powerful orgasmic experience and copious amounts of cum that will exit their balls through prostate stimulation, so become his sexual pioneer and discover it for him. He'll think you're the Goddess of Sex. (read chapter *VI: The Dexterity of Bootie Worship*)

9. Exceptional Sex is a complete package of smell, touch, taste, sound and sight.

A) *Always **Smell** wonderful* and make sure that the way you smell is to his liking, and does not bring back any 'reminders' of the woman who was with him before you.

One man who emailed me for advice was truly upset because he liked the new woman he was dating, but she 'reminded' him of his ex-wife and he couldn't figure out why. According to him, she *was nothing* like his ex-wife, whom he had divorced five years earlier! Turns out that the new woman he was dating wore the exact same perfume his ex-wife had worn!

Smell is so important that Scientists have proven that the combined scents of Lavender and Cinnamon are guaranteed to get your man Hard-n-ready for sex. So make sure you exploit the power of smell, and make it work for you and not against you.

B) *Sweetly and knowledgeably **touch** him*, because it matters. I have a unique, non-sexual touch I use with a man and I know that he misses it when he is not with me. He cannot identify what it is that he is so significantly missing about me. Just one of my little tricks.

Your man is really just a little boy, and your endearing touch is vital to his emotional well-being. So, touch him sweetly and touch him often.

C) **Taste** delicious and make the effort to always keep your pussy clean and healthy. Too many men are pussy-shy when it comes to giving a woman oral sex because they've had a really foul experience with a woman in the past. There are all kinds of sprays and lotions and potions to spice-up oral sex. If you want him to lick your pussy, make it taste like his favorite beer or favorite snack-food! I have a friend who puts cookie-dough ice-cream on her pussy for her man to eat off. There are no limits, okay?! Just use your imagination and give him a reason to lick you up. Try frozen orange juice, or slide a cinnamon candy a short distance into your pussy.

D) **Sound** energetic and sexy in bed, and ask him what he wants to hear or what he's in the mood for. You don't need to scream and moan and thrash around like a porn star unless that's what he asks for, but, please articulate something!

E) Be alluring in his **Sight** and wear sexy apparel to bed. You don't need to dress-up like a vamp every night-of-the-week, but going to bed in a stained sweatshirt or granny nightgown is a real mood killer - even if he *isn't* in-the-mood.

You can find and purchase sweet and sexy bedclothes from lacy-long john fashions to silky, long-sleeve nighties. There is something for every personality. It doesn't take a lot of work to feel sexy or even be sexy all it takes is an attempt! You did it to get him. You need to be consistent to keep him. (read chapter *VI: Erotic Accessories*)

coresexcoresexcoresexcoresexcoresexcoresexcoresexcoresexcoresexco
resexcoresexcoresexcoresexcoresexcoresexcoresexcoresexcoresexcore
sexcoresexcoresexcoresexcoresexcoresexcoresexcoresexcoresexcorese
xcoresexcoresexcoresexcoresexcoresexcoresexcoresexcoresexcoresexc
oresexcoresexcoresexcoresexcoresexcoresexcoresexcoresexcoresexcor
esexcoresexcoresexcoresexcoresexcoresexcoresexcoresexcoresexcores
excoresexcoresexcoresexcoresexcoresexcoresexcoresexcoresexcoresex
coresexcoresexcoresexcoresexcoresexcoresexcoresexcoresexcoresexco
resexcoresexcoresexcoresexcoresexcoresexcoresexcoresexcoresexcore
sexcoresexcoresexcoresexcoresexcoresexcoresexcoresexcoresexcorese
xcoresexcoresexcoresexcoresexcoresexcoresexcoresexcoresexcoresexc
oresexcoresexcoresexcoresexcoresexcoresexcoresexcoresexcoresexcor
esexcoresexcoresexcoresexcoresexcoresexcoresexcoresexcoresexcores
excoresexcoresexcoresexcoresexcoresexcoresexcoresexcoresexcoresex

On: Creating that Core Sex Connection

coresexcoresexcoresexcoresexcoresexcoresexcoresexcoresexcoresexco
resexcoresexcoresexcoresexcoresexcoresexcoresexcoresexcoresexcore
sexcoresexcoresexcoresexcoresexcoresexcoresexcoresexcoresexcorese
xcoresexcoresexcoresexcoresexcoresexcoresexcoresexcoresexcoresexc
oresexcoresexcoresexcoresexcoresexcoresexcoresexcoresexcoresexcor
esexcoresexcoresexcoresexcoresexcoresexcoresexcoresexcoresexcores
excoresexcoresexcoresexcoresexcoresexcoresexcoresexcoresexcoresex
coresexcoresexcoresexcoresexcoresexcoresexcoresexcoresexcoresexco
resexcoresexcoresexcoresexcoresexcoresexcoresexcoresexcoresexcore
sexcoresexcoresexcoresexcoresexcoresexcoresexcoresexcoresexcorese
xcoresexcoresexcoresexcoresexcoresexcoresexcoresexcoresexcoresexc
oresexcoresexcoresexcoresexcoresexcoresexcoresexcoresexcoresexcor
esexcoresexcoresexcoresexcoresexcoresexcoresexcoresexcoresexcores
excoresexcoresexcoresexcoresexcoresexcoresexcoresexcoresexcoresex
coresexcoresexcoresexcoresexcoresexcoresexcoresexcoresexcoresexco
resexcoresexcoresexcoresexcoresexcoresexcoresexcoresexcoresexcore
sexcoresexcoresexcoresexcoresexcoresexcoresexcoresexcoresexcorese
xcoresexcoresexcoresexcoresexcoresexcoresexcoresexcoresexcoresexc
oresexcoresexcoresexcoresexcoresexcoresexcoresexcoresexcoresexcor
esexcoresexcoresexcoresexcoresexcoresexcoresexcoresexcoresexcores
excoresexcoresexcoresexcoresexcoresexcoresexcoresexcoresexcoresex
coresexcoresexcoresexcoresexcoresexcoresexcoresexcoresexcoresexco
resexcoresexcoresexcoresexcoresexcoresexcoresexcoresexcoresexcore
sexcoresexcoresexcoresexcoresexcoresexcoresexcoresexcoresexcorese
xcoresexcoresexcoresexcoresexcoresexcoresexcoresexcoresexcoresexc
oresexcoresexcoresexcoresexcoresexcoresexcoresexcoresexcoresexcor
esexcoresexcoresexcoresexcoresexcoresexcoresexcoresexcoresexcores
excoresexcoresexcoresexcoresexcoresexcoresexcoresexcoresexcoresex
coresexcoresexcoresexcoresexcoresexcoresexcoresexcoresexcoresexco
resexcoresexcoresexcoresexcoresexcoresexcoresexcoresexcoresexcore
sexcoresexcoresexcoresexcoresexcoresexcoresexcoresexcoresexcorese
xcoresexcoresexcoresexcoresexcoresexcoresexcoresexcoresexcoresexc
oresexcoresexcoresexcoresexcoresexcoresexcoresexcoresexcoresexcor
esexcoresexcoresexcoresexcoresexcoresexcoresexcoresexcoresexcores
excoresexcoresexcoresexcoresexcoresexcoresexcoresexcoresexcoresex
coresexcoresexcoresexcoresexcoresexcoresexcoresexcoresexcoresexco
resexcoresexcoresexcoresexcoresexcoresexcoresexcoresexcoresexcore
sexcoresexcoresexcoresexcoresexcoresexcoresexcoresexcoresexcorese
xcoresexcoresexcoresexcoresexcoresexcoresexcoresexcoresexcoresexc
oresexcoresexcoresexcoresexcoresexcoresexcoresexcoresexcoresexcor
esexcoresexcoresexcoresexcoresexcoresexcoresexcoresexcoresexcores
excoresexcoresexcoresexcoresexcoresexcoresexcoresexcoresexcoresex

XII. Creating that Core Sex Connection

We tend to think of the erotic as an easy tantalizing sexual arousal. I speak of the erotic as the deepest Life Force; a force which moves up toward living in a fundamental way.

~~~Andre Lorde

Artwork featured at: www.gradiva.com

Across the chasm of murky vagueness in every Romantic Relationship, is the transparent reality of what It is:

The Female is the Blood and Nerve.

The Male is the Bone and Skin.

Without Blood and Nerve, Bone and Skin could not feel.

Without Bone and Skin, Blood and Nerve could not maintain.

Despite all my expertise, and for all that I know about men and sex and relationships - I can be like every other woman at times - sometimes, I don't really listen to my man - more-or-less, I can be like the cobbler whose children have no shoes.

There were times when a man will say "I really need you." I never understood what he was struggling to explain to me, until something happened that forced me to make the connection between how he felt when he asserted that he needed me, and who he became after he'd entered me. And like every piece-of-the-puzzle, the magnificence of it all eventually fell into place.

A man comes to me drained and frustrated, in thin-skinned pain, his male emotional-carriage held-fast and strong; so true to his gender, all tied-up and completely inaccessible and impenetrable like a good little soldier.

After he had entered me, after he had released whatever was tied-up and inaccessible in his soul... his entire being would visibly relax to his very Core. All his drained frustrated thin-skinned pain... departed. The man who had come to my house had been expelled the moment he'd fused his body to mine.

That Need of his, was to connect with me.

Because I am the woman who adores him, worships him, believes in him.

Loves him.

There is lazy-this-is-our-routine-Saturday sex... there is that-quick-fuck-in-the-shower sex... there is it's-okay now-I've-done-the-dishes-and-the-kids-are-finally-asleep sex. Whatever the reason or the occasion, most sex is Nothing Sex... Fast-Food Sex for an undernourished Steak-Starved soul.

You are not just an object to your man of sex, or simply a representation of All that is Female. *You are a need*. If you cannot understand his need, then you can never expect him to try and understand you.

Often, your man isn't aware of what he feels; he doesn't have an 'informed definition' in his Male DNA for what he craves... he just sees that what he 'needs', he can only get with, and from, you - because your sex is the balm that heals his soul. If you choose, from this day forward, to create That Bond with him, where sex becomes a pleasure and a choice and no longer a complaint or a stop-watch where you ask him: "Do we have to Do It tonight?" or "Aren't you finished yet?" Your entire romantic relationship will take a turn for The Beginning.

To take your man's body and fuck him beyond his past, ahead of his present, and into his future... To fulfill your man's Fundamental Need to connect with only you that one woman who has the power to heal, restore, mend, revive his soul and touch him in such a way that it generates him to feel Right...

That is the creation of Core Sex.

Creative Screwing

toeringswigscrotchlesspantiesnippleringsmerrywidowstatoostoerings
wigscrotchlesspantiesnippleringsmerrywidowstatoostoeringswigscrot
chlesspantiesnippleringsmerrywidowstatoostoeringswigscrotchlesspa
ntiesnippleringsmerrywidowstatoostoeringswigscrotchlesspantiesnip
pleringsmerrywidowstatoostoeringswigscrotchlesspantiesnipplerings
merrywidowstatoostoeringswigscrotchlesspantiesnippleringsmerrywid
owstatoostoeringswigscrotchlesspantiesnippleringsmerrywidowstatoo
stoeringswigscrotchlesspantiesnippleringsmerrywidowstatoostoering
swigscrotchlesspantiesnippleringsmerrywidowstatoostoeringswigscro
tchlesspantiesnippleringsmerrywidowstatoostoeringswigscrotchlessp
antiesnippleringsmerrywidowstatoostoeringswigscrotchlesspantiesni
ppleringsmerrywidowstatoostoeringswigscrotchlesspantiesnipplering
smerrywidowstatoostoeringswigscrotchlesspantiesnippleringsmerrywi
dowstatoostoeringswigscrotchlesspantiesnippleringsmerrywidowstato
ostoeringswigscrotchlesspantiesnippleringsmerrywidowstatoostoerin
gswigscrotchlesspantiesnippleringsmerrywidowstatoostoeringswigscr
otchlesspantiesnippleringsmerrywidowstatoostoeringswigscrotchless

Erotic Accessories

pantiesnippleringsmerrywidowstatoostoeringswigscrotchlesspantiesn
ippleringsmerrywidowstatoostoeringswigscrotchlesspantiesnipplerin
gsmerrywidowstatoostoeringswigscrotchlesspantiesnippleringsmerryw
idowstatoostoeringswigscrotchlesspantiesnippleringsmerrywidowstat
oostoeringswigscrotchlesspantiesnippleringsmerrywidowstatoostoeri
ngswigscrotchlesspantiesnippleringsmerrywidowstatoostoeringswigsc
rotchlesspantiesnippleringsmerrywidowstatoostoeringswigscrotchles
spantiesnippleringsmerrywidowstatoostoeringswigscrotchlesspanties
nippleringsmerrywidowstatoostoeringswigscrotchlesspantiesnippleri
ngsmerrywidowstatoostoeringswigscrotchlesspantiesnippleringsmerry
widowstatoostoeringswigscrotchlesspantiesnippleringsmerrywidowsta
toostoeringswigscrotchlesspantiesnippleringsmerrywidowstatoostoer
ingswigscrotchlesspantiesnippleringsmerrywidowstatoostoeringswigs
crotchlesspantiesnippleringsmerrywidowstatoostoeringswigscrotchle
sspantiesnippleringsmerrywidowstatoostoeringswigscrotchlesspantie
snippleringsmerrywidowstatoostoeringswigscrotchlesspantiesnippler
ingsmerrywidowstatoostoeringswigscrotchlesspantiesnippleringsmerr
ywidowstatoostoeringswigscrotchlesspantiesnippleringsmerrywidowst
atoostoeringswigscrotchlesspantiesnippleringsmerrywidowstatoostoe
ringswigscrotchlesspantiesnippleringsmerrywidowstatoostoeringswig
scrotchlesspantiesnippleringsmerrywidowstatoostoeringswigscrotchl
esspantiesnippleringsmerrywidowstatoostoeringswigscrotchlesspanti
esnippleringsmerrywidowstatoostoeringswigscrotchlesspantiesnipple
ringsmerrywidowstatoostoeringswigscrotchlesspantiesnippleringsmer
rywidowstatoostoeringswigscrotchlesspantiesnippleringsmerrywidows
tatoostoeringswigscrotchlesspantiesnippleringsmerrywidowstatoosto
eringswigscrotchlesspantiesnippleringsmerrywidowstatoostoeringswi
gscrotchlesspantiesnippleringsmerrywidowstatoostoeringswigscrotch
lesspantiesnippleringsmerrywidowstatoostoeringswigscrotchlesspant
iesnippleringsmerrywidowstatoostoeringswigscrotchlesspantiesnippl
eringsmerrywidowstatoostoeringswigscrotchlesspantiesnippleringsme
rrywidowstatoostoeringswigscrotchlesspantiesnippleringsmerrywidow
statoostoeringswigscrotchlesspantiesnippleringsmerrywidowstatoost
oeringswigscrotchlesspantiesnippleringsmerrywidowstatoostoeringsw
igscrotchlesspantiesnippleringsmerrywidowstatoostoeringswigscrotc
hlesspantiesnippleringsmerrywidowstatoostoeringswigscrotchlesspan
tiesnippleringsmerrywidowstatoostoeringswigscrotchlesspantiesnipp
leringsmerrywidowstatoostoeringswigscrotchlesspantiesnippleringsm
rrywidowstatoostoeringswigscrotchlesspantiesnippleringsmerrywidow

136

XIII. Erotic Accessories

*To dance confidently in fringe panties when you are
five-four with cellulite, is a great thing.*

~~~Drew Barrymore

Every Goddess needs a prop. No matter how hot the sex is
between him and you, eventually, Great Sex diminishes into
Really-in-a-Rut. If you were to compare your sex life to
eating dinner, just imagine what it would be like to eat the
very same meal every single night for the next twenty years.

That is how your man sees sex with you: invariable,
uninteresting, yawn-boring, repetitive and monotonous.
When you get naked, he knows exactly what kind of sex he's
going to get from you. Every. Single. Time.

Women often complain that men cease being romantic
after a relationship settles-in, but I believe men cease being
romantic because women stop being sexy. Men
continuously describe monogamous-sex as ."... invariable,

uninteresting, yawn-boring, repetitive, monotonous sex..."
usually followed with "... I just wish she'd try and spice
things up a bit, like she did when she was dating me."

If you really want your sex with him to be the best he's ever
had... if you truly want him to be thinking about you at the
office instead of his boss's new leggy blond assistant, than
you need to do what it takes to make that thing happen.

So, spend some quality time researching the following...

Naughtyware:

I cannot stress this enough: a man loves it when a woman
dresses-up for sex. Even if you were to just put on a pair of
thigh-high stockings and high heels, it would drive him
nuts.

I'm sure many of the women reading this book are far from
a size 6 so let me clue you in: I hover between a size 14 and
a size 16, I am almost 6'ft tall (think: Amazon Chick) and I
have tons of sexy stuff, because it all comes in sizes ranging
from 0-50... so I don't want to hear any of your excuses! Put
this book down right after reading this chapter, and go out
and buy some fancy panties for your big butt right now!
He's going to see your ass anyway, so you might as well
prance around in pretty panties instead of ultra-boring
white cotton briefs!

 Wigs... wearing a wig can give him the thrill of
bedding a mysterious woman. It will also make you
feel more daring and risqué! Wigs are made from
real or synthetic hair, in colors you never even
knew existed, and are made in styles and length from punk-
rock short, to Lady Godiva long.

Costumes... from a French Maid to Girl Scout, Taxi Driver, Navy Seal, Harem Girl, Cat Woman or FBI Agent - there is a costume for it! Unearth his kinky-fun fetish, or whatever else that turns him on when it comes to dress-up, and order a costume from one of the many online shops at the end of this chapter. Not only is it entertaining for him, but wearing a costume can make you feel powerful, as well as thoroughly sexy!

If you want more of a sexually-creative kick, get online and shop the utterly unsurpassed www.electriqueboutique.com internet store, which has *every* Erotic Accessory imaginable. They have so much to offer your sexual imagination that it will take you roughly three hours just to skim through the site. There are many items that will totally spill his sexual imagination overboard!

 Sexy Nightwear... most lingerie companies now offer you an array of loungewear that is so sexy and reveling, it makes the whole idea of staying - in an adventure. Purchase a few of these pretty items and wear them on a night when nothing exciting will happen... except you!

 Garters... stockings and garters should be a staple in any woman's boudoir, and now companies like Victoria's Secret offer all kinds of options when it comes to hooking-up a garter! You can find sexy garters anywhere.

 Half-Slips... this is such a smart and sexy idea, I wish I could meet the designer! Half-Slips are flirty, provocative and can be worn-sexy in several different ways.

Babydolls... featured in fabrics from comfy-cotton to lacy-marabou, BabyDoll nighties come is so many different styles and varieties from Silky-Romantic to PVC-Nasty that this sort of lingerie is what appeals to most women. And to most men!

 Pretty Panties... you can find sexy sweet pretty-pretty panties everywhere from Wal-Mart Superstores in Arkansas, to LaPerla Lingerie in Italy and you can buy sexy sweet pretty-pretty panties in every style, size and material. So if you do not own incredibly countless pairs sexy sweet pretty-pretty panties, then now is where you start!

 Nightslips... nothing that even comes close to resembling your great-grandmother's nightgowns! The newly fashioned Nightslips are a sexy I-want-to-fuck-you version of a comfortable old favorites, and some of the sexiest styles are actually made out of cozy flannel. So, what is your excuse for not having sexy Nightslips?

 Merry Widows... sexually delightful, divine and exquisite; Merry Widows are a throw-back from the 1800's when women wore them for necessity, rather than pleasure. A Merry Widow gives you every advantage: it tucks in your tummy, makes a beautiful fleshy avalanche out of your breasts, and accents the 'V' between your legs.

Bustier Sets... these sets come in such a numerous amount of lovely styles, it is really difficult to pick-out just one! From 100% silk to all-out-lace, the best thing about Bustiers is that they are made to accentuate what you've got and camouflage what you'd rather not have! Because Bustier Sets come in so many different designs, it will really be easy for you to find one that fits your body-type to perfection.

Body Jewelry:

Now you can find ways to decorate every part of your body, no piercing required! You ought to wear fancy toes rings and ankle bracelets or add-on fake tattoos that can be brush or stuck onto the small of your back or next-to your nipple; use Bindi Jewels that you can press-on to your nose or near the corners of your eyes; enhance your belly with adhesive belly-button rings or tummy chains; make your nipples pretty with rings, nipple blusher or pasties... it's out there if you want to try it! Just go to any of the online sex shops in this chapter, and explore all the ways that you can make your body gorgeous!

 Lacey Heart Pasties... these red retro lace designs are perfect for showing off your nipples without revealing them! Peel off the backing and waltz around the house! www.adameve.com

 Nipple Charm... dazzle him with one – or two – of these hand-crafted 1" diameter sterling silver charms! It's easy position nipple in center, and then gently squeeze the charm until it stays on. Not only does this charm show-off your nipples, but it keeps them hard and erect. www.adameve.com

Showgirl Nipple Tassels... spotlight your lovely nipples with these sexy tassels! Rubber-tipped fasteners are adjustable for total comfort and the tassels give a sensual, classy look that will really turn his head. www.adameve.com

Clit Clip... passionate, stimulating and easy to slip on and wear! Adjustable, and just a little lube helps this unique genital jewelry stay put. Eight pretty dangling red translucent beads fuel the fantasy. www.adameve.com

Lotions and Potions:

There are sooooooo many lotion and potion products from tasty anal lubes to flavored massage oils that what it really comes down to, is your personal taste and what works for you and him. For instance, there is certain Pina Colada oil that I personally think tastes yucky, but I have a friend that loves to smother it all over her husband's cock before she gives him Head! The lubes I've recommend below are what my friends and I all neutrally agree on but to find what works best for the two of you, you need to try out many products and explore all the possibilities available to you.

Kama Sutra Products... sensual pleasures for the bedroom and the bath, these top-of-the-line products are the best that you will find anywhere. Massage oils that smell like Sweet Almond; Oils of Love from Chocolate Mint to Cherry Almond; Honey Dust that tastes as sweet as it feels, edible Massage Cream you'll want to lick off his body; minty Pleasure Balm that will light-up his cock like a rocket. After Bath body oils, bathing kits, body lotions and bathing bars for After-Sex glow. Kama Sutra Products even has the lovely Bedside Box, Gift Drum and The Weekender, to make your daily or get-away lovemaking a fucking sensation. www.babeland.com

Chocolate Body Creams... tastes lovely and yummy just like chocolate, without the all the mess. www.babeland.com, www.chocolatefantisies.com

Flavored Body Powders... use the feather and brush his entire body with one of these many fruit flavored body powers, and then lick it off him. Most of these products really taste yummy. www.babeland.com, www.chocolatefantisies.com

Edible Body Crayons/Paints/Tattoos... you can trace his cock with cherry-flavored paint or write a poem on his back with lemon flavored paint just use your imagination and go with it. These products strive to give you the best-taste. www.babeland.com, www.chocolatefantisies.com

Cum Better:

You can purchase orgasm-enhancing products that will help you *never miss again* when you are about to come. The products I have featured below work so well, that if you apply them before sex and then move into the Missionary Position or On Top during vaginal intercourse, you will come while he is inside of you and it will feel like a splash of fireworks on the Fourth of July.

There are many products on the sex-market that will make you come better. Please look them over and read what other female users have to say, then try them out and find the one that really works for you. When you come, not only does it give you an immense physical and emotional release, but it gives him a feeling of accomplishment.

 Scream Kreem... brings back the sensation that your body craves without harmful side effects or costly prescriptions. Just rub a small amount on your clit for increased stimulation. I personally know the inventor of *Scream Kreem*; he is a colleague of mine and a talented chemist who cares about what it takes to make a woman come so it isn't any wonder that his wife adores him! Of all products along this theme on the market, *Scream Kreem* is the Most excellent. It works just as well for Post-Menopausal women, as it does for 22-year-old girls. www.screamkreem.com

 Eve's Ecstasy Cream... jump-start your intimate moments with a little dab of this special formula it will awaken the pleasure nerves in your clit. This is another product that works like a dream one of my best friends swears that it took her marriage from lackluster to lust! www.adameve.com

Make Me Cum Gel... rub it into your clit and it will get you off when you rub yourself into him. You will come harder and take pleasure in longer-lasting sex after you've put a dab of this gel on your clit, because it was specially formulated for any woman who wants to heighten her orgasmic sensitivity. www.adameve.com

G-Spot Gel... this innovative formula with naturally active ingredients increases the sensitivity of your G-spot and temporarily enlarges your G-spot, so that it is easier to find when stimulated through intercourse or via a vibrator. It definitely will help you discover a new dimension of orgasm! www.kinglove.com

Vibrel™... this is an OTC (Over The Counter), intimacy enhancing lubricant applied directly to the vagina and the clitoris uniquely designed to increase a woman's sexual sensation. *Vibrel™* is designed to be used alone or with a partner. The *Vibrel™* formulation helps women enjoy the intimacy of masturbation or sexual intercourse. *Vibrel™* is designed for use by women only. It does not have an effect on men. Developed by the biochemists at *GlycoBioSciences, Inc.* (GBS), *Vibrel™* Intimate Feminine Lubricant is an aqueous, slightly viscous gel that contains the vitamin Niacin as one of its ingredients. Each tube contains a total of 3 ml of the product good for 3 to 5 individual applications per tube. www.vibrel.com

Tighten Your Pussy:

I have personally advised many women who have had the problem of tightness-loss in their vagina to seek an assist, because having a baby and/or the aging process really ruins vaginal elasticity, and while the products listed below are only temporary-tighteners, these products *really* perform very, very well 'in the moment'.

Like everything else on the market, you need to find the product that works best for you. If you should try two of these products and find that neither work as you'd anticipated, please do not get discouraged and give-up. Simply move-on to other products in this area until you find the one that performs to your (and to his) satisfaction.

 Harmony Cream... specially created for women, Harmony Cream has been used over centuries by women in Asia. *Harmony Cream is the 100% natural herb-based cream that can tighten your vagina naturally in just 20 seconds.* Harmony Cream has been scientifically proven to effectively tighten your vagina, giving you and your partner increased sexual intimacy and pleasures. www.tightpleasure.com

 Hold Tight Crème... if you want that tight, first-time feeling, this exciting crème works to reduce and tighten the vaginal walls for tight, sweetly snug strokes. Simply massage a small amount into your vaginal walls, and then wait about fifteen minutes before intercourse. He will notice the difference, and so will you. www.babeland.com

 Liquid Virgin... feel like a virgin again with a few drops of this contracting lubricant! Apply the cherry-scented liquid to your labial area 15 minutes before intercourse, then enjoy the tightening, wet sensation it brings. You will actually feel your vaginal muscles tighten and contract. www.adameve.com

Vaginal-Rejuvenation Surgeries:

Due to laser technology and other minimally invasive advances in medical care, women are now able to transform and strengthen their bodies to make life more comfortable and more enjoyable. Vaginal rejuvenation, hymenoplasty, *and* labiaplasty *are three treatments currently available to women who wish to change the shape of vaginal areas as well as strengthen pelvic floor muscles. Strengthening the structure and support within the lower pelvic region is effective at minimizing or eliminating urinary incontinence and helps to make sexuality more satisfactory for some women. www.OnlineSurgery.com unites individuals with local cosmetic surgeons who are experienced with women's health concerns and who offer a variety of treatments specifically tailored to meet the unique needs of female patients. Some procedures offered by surgeons include:*

Designer Laser Vaginoplasty, GSpotAmplification, Hymenoplasty, Labiaplasty, Laser Vaginal Rejuvenation, Vaginal Rejuvenation, Vaginal Relaxation.

(Narration is taken from www.OnlineSurgery.com)

Great Cock Creams:

If you want to become *The Cock Queen*, then do your hand magic on him by using one of these boy-products, whenever you stroke his cock. The following hand-job products listed below produce better cum results than regular lotions, oils or lubes when used for masturbation because they are *specifically* made for The Man and His Cock.

 Stroke29... this thick, creamy lubricant takes on the "heat and glide of aroused human tissue." The heavy, face-cream consistency stays exactly where you put it, but becomes slippery with use, adding delicious sensation without being so wet you'll lose your grip on him. And, it is long lasting. www.babeland.com

Boy Butter... spreads on with ease, lasts a long time, and washes off with plain water. *Oils in the cream make it incompatible with latex condoms and with vaginas*, but if you stroke his cock with this, he will be screaming your name. Just remember: use a wipe on his cock before he takes a dip inside your pussy! www.babeland.com

Outstanding Lubricants:

Every lubricant *is not the same*... some are exceptional and some are so awful it'll make you wonder who would buy it twice! When it comes to lubes, you really have to go on an expedition until you find a few that work like slick!

 Liquid Silk... this creamy lube is a favorite because it has no glycerin, which means that it won't get as sticky as other water-based lubes. *The slightly bitter taste rules it out for oral sex*, but it's perfect for anything else you can think of! www.babeland.com

 Sensual Power... is water-based, latex compatible and glycerin free (making it more vagina-friendly than lubes with sugars). Slick, but not sticky, this lube gets the thumbs up from oral sex fans who find it practically tasteless! www.babeland.com

 Astroglide... treat yourself to a "glide" of silky smooth penetration. Just a tiny amount no more than a half teaspoon of this deluxe sex lube goes a long way! www.condomania.com

Vibra Glide Lube... this sensual gel lube is fairly new, and one of the best products I have ever used. My man is partial to it, and he always detects when I've run out and have to use another product... it's that good! www.adameve.com

Slippery Stuff Gel... specially blended to feel like your body's own natural juices, Slippery Stuff Gel can be used safely with condoms. www.adameve.com

Astroglid Silk... this is makes the "glide" of silky smooth penetration. This deluxe sex lube goes a long way! www.babeland.com

Spring Water Personal Lube... this water-based lubricant that makes you stay wetter longer, with a clean, fresh feeling too! Latex compatible only. www.adameve.com

Elbow Grease Gel... this industrial strength formula is THICK and it lasts all night. Made especially for rough sex! So, if you're going to play hard, this is the lube of Champions! www.babeland.com

PrePair Lubricant... is scientifically formulated sex lubricant that's slippery smooth, odorless and tasteless. www.adameve.com

Fantasy Gear Kits:

Almost every sex shop you visit online will have wonderful fantasy kits that release your sexual imagination. From bondage kits to romantic evening kits, you really can find anything you need, all in one pretty box. The following kits are featured at the online sex shops www.babeland.com and www.adameve.com

Spank Me Kit... set the mood and make your partner's pulse quicken! All you need is a room: light the tea lights then alternate sensations with the warming massage oil and peppermint cooling cream! www.adameve.com

The Mile High Kit... has everything you might need for spur-of-the-moment sex; be prepared for anything from a one-hour layover to a long, romantic evening. Contents include a handy "Do Not Disturb" sign, massage oil, a wireless bullet vibe, a bright blue mini feather tickler, a blue mega-stretch cock ring, a silky fabric-lined blindfold, water-based lube and three condoms. Cleansing cloths, breath mints, and a small makeup mirror help you and your partner tidy up. www.babeland.com

Foot Fantasy Kit... Admire her tasty toes? Enjoy the curve of her arches? Live your taboo fantasies with this playful kit created to celebrate her erotic feet. www.adameve.com

Liquid Latex Starter Kit... Liquid Latex glides on over skin and dries in minutes, and unlike body paint allows the skin to breathe. It's also good for decorating the handles of canes and slappers. Sprinkle on a little stardust for maximum glam. This kit provides everything you need to make a fetish outfit to remember: 8 ounces each of black latex and red latex, 1/4 ounce jars of silver and red stardust, a variety of applicators, and an instruction booklet. Not recommended for people with latex or other chemical sensitivities. www.babeland.com

Do-It-Yourself-Adult-Movie Kit... all You Need Is a Camera! Act out your wildest XXX fantasies––in the privacy of your home! Includes script ideas, a 6 1/2" variable speed body massager as a "prop," and an adult video to get you started on your own fantasy! www.adameve.com

Romance Him Kit... a little relaxation and sensual indulgence can help boost a flagging libido, so pamper him with the items in this bath and body kit. This aromatherapy-based collection contains bath milk, massage oil, and a scented candle; the fragrance of ylang-ylang and Mandarin can be arousing, while the cinnamon-scented oils warm the skin. The bath milk contains milk, sea salt and essential oils; massage oil is based on safflower/sunflower oils. (Not recommended for people with fragrance sensitivities) www.babeland.com

Clone Your Pussy Kit... immortalize your pussy just like the porn stars do! This kit has everything you need, and it's so easy! Just mix the molding powder, hold the molding container against your pussy, and easily pull it off! He will LOVE this idea, because he'll never expect something so intimate and personal from you! www.adameve.com

Clone His Cock Kit... make a vibrating rubber copy of his cock right in your own home! *1 AA Battery not incl. Make a totally edible Melt & Mold Vanilla or Chocolate Copy of any penis. Deliciously erotic, amazing detail! www.clone-a-willy.com

Spank Me, Tie Me, Boss Me Toys:

If you've ever wanted your man to bend you over his knee and smack your ass or if he's ever mentioned how he'd love to tie you to the bed posts or if the two of you have ever talked about your donning a pair of leather boots and ordering him around then the following products are just a small window into the great world of Spanking, Bondage and S/M. I have included some great books on all three subjects, so that you can explore these Other Worlds, directed by the experts who know their craft.

Elk Hide Floggers... these beautiful handmade leather floggers are bound to feel fantastic when he whips your bootie. The Elk hide flogger is soft and dense to the touch – its black leather tails provide a light sting and a moderately heavy thud with grip. The purple and black tails of the lighter weight Deer hide flogger provide a gentler thud. www.babeland.com

Star Paddle... he can spank your fanny well with this slightly curved, star-struck paddle. www.babeland.com

 Nipple Clamps... send sparks to your nipples when you hook them up for S/M play, to these comfortable, stainless-steel clamps. www.babeland.com

 Body Harness... strap-up for an S/M adventure in this comfortable leather body harness, with hand cuffs. www.babeland.com

 Door Jam Cuffs... Just lay the weighted straps over door, close it shut and turn any room into a playground for kinky bondage play! Tease or please, control or be controlled. Now it's easy! www.adameve.com

 **Love Bonds**... enjoy the "bonding" experience! This deluxe set of wrist, ankle restraints and blindfold will satisfy you and your willing partner's fantasies. These are made of high quality artificial fur and strong nylon. www.adameve.com

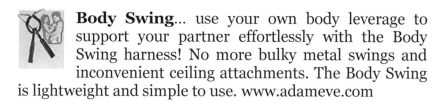 **Body Swing**... use your own body leverage to support your partner effortlessly with the Body Swing harness! No more bulky metal swings and inconvenient ceiling attachments. The Body Swing is lightweight and simple to use. www.adameve.com

Love Swing™ & Universal Stand... once you try this sex swing & stand, you'll wonder how you ever got along without IT! It's ready to use right out of the box! Stand, sit or squat it's your choice! www.adameve.com

 Secure Sling... say goodbye to gravity as secure suspension allows your mind and body to relax to a more receptive state. Three-inch webbing reinforced stitching, steel D-rings, comfortable, adjustable leather stirrups. www.babeland.com

Wonderful Reads:

 Flogging... new to sensation play? By Joseph Bean. Pick up this classic work on whip-wielding. Joseph Bean clearly explains the basics, from shopping for floggers to different styles of whipping. The erotic vignettes demonstrate not only safety techniques, but ways to set the stage for a really hot scene.

The Erotic Bondage Book, by Jay Wiseman... want to learn the ropes? Jay Wiseman's accessible primer is an essential guide to safe bondage. Wiseman's thorough, easy-to-follow instructions with elegant pencil illustrations are geared for men and women of all sexualities and many different body types. The handbook includes detailed lessons covering breast and genital bondage, body harnesses, hog ties and other special techniques.

SM 101, by Jay Wiseman... This exhaustive "how-to" book has taught the fundamentals of safe, exciting SM to tens of thousands of people of all genders and orientations.

 Screw the Roses, Send Me the Thorns: The Romance and Sexual Sorcery of Sadomasochism, by Phillip Miller, Molly Devon, and William A. Granzig... this guide to S/M play is one of the best. Fun and informative, covering all relative subjects and easy to read, this book is highly recommended. Great for learning to tie knots, negotiations and a great glossary.

 Sensuous Magic, by Pat Califia... for anyone who harbors fantasies of erotic dominance and submission, Sensuous Magic is our best guide to BD/SM. Mixing wickedly erotic vignettes with practical how-to suggestions and personal insight, the whip-smart Califia offers seasoned advice to couples of all orientations. Get inspiration to identify what you want and how to get it. Subjects include communication and negotiation, psychology of bondage, topping techniques (including tickling, pressure, temperature, and impact play), whipping, and sex in S/M scenes, electrical play, play piercing and more. Experienced players will appreciate the breadth of Califia's knowledge of S/M safety and technique and his insights into the psychology of S/M. Novices will be encouraged by Califia's honest, unpretentious approach. www.babeland.com

When Someone You Love Is Kinky, by Dossie Easton and Catherine A. Liszt... about one in ten Americans is involved with bondage, spanking, erotic role-play, body modification or other unconventional lifestyles. Now, for anyone who's ever overheard a conversation, glimpsed a toy, or been startled by a tattoo, there's "*When Someone You Love Is Kinky*," a sympathetic and comprehensive handbook for helping you understand the behaviors and lifestyles of the people you care about.

 The Ultimate Guide to Sexual Fantasy: How to Turn Your Fantasies into Reality, by Violet Blue... with wit and enthusiasm, sex educator Violet Blue encourages couples to talk about and explore fantasies together to deepen erotic intimacy. She takes readers on a tour of the wide world of sexual fantasies, offering expert advice for talking dirty to a partner, playing with toys and dress-up, making homemade porn, and exploring fetishes, sex scenes, phone sex, and much more.

 The Many Joys of Sex Toys: The Ultimate How-to Handbook for Couples and Singles, by Anne Seamns... ignite your sex life with 100 easy-to-learn sex toy techniques! This illustrated, definitive guide will show you how to choose, buy, and have a creative blast with your sex toys.

Sexy Mood Makers:

The most wonderful thing about the Internet is that it allows us to reach so many places we would otherwise never go. Women are so busy; we have children, jobs, pets, and men who need more attention than the kids, pets and job combined! So, there is nothing more fantastic than the invention of the Internet, which connects women to worlds far beyond our limited time or vehicle mileage. If you explore and use the Internet for all it's worth, you will find sexual opportunities *on every online sex shop* that can take your romantic relationship with your man from dull to *passionate* with thousands of hot ideas that will make It last and last and last. Promise!

 The Liberator... Ramp up your partner play, reduce body pain and turn your whole house into a sex playground with this new sex furniture. The large Ramp is designed to provide support for bottoms-up adventures, or to support your entire upper body for face forward fun. Get comfy for longer sessions of partner sex, spanking, flogging and rear-entry delights. Combine it with the Wedge for a wider variety of sex positions. The padded core offers stability and cushion for extended comfort. Don't worry about making a mess, it comes with machine washable outer cover, nylon inner cover and discreet nylon carrying bag for travel and storage. www.liberator.com

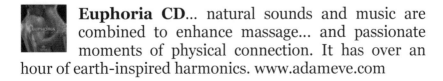 **Indulgence CD**... created especially for lovemaking, here's an irresistible backbeat for passion. Sensual elements from world music are fused with jazz. Indulge yourself in an hour of opulent sound. www.adameve.com

Euphoria CD... natural sounds and music are combined to enhance massage... and passionate moments of physical connection. It has over an hour of earth-inspired harmonics. www.adameve.com

Surrender CD... Invoke sultry heat and sensual exploring. Answer the call of the horns as they beckon you to your desires. Over 60 minutes. www.adameve.com

 Glow In The Dark Bubble Bath... charge up tubby time! Hold bottle to strong light, and then pour in as you would any bubble bath mix. Douse the lights and enjoy the glow! www.adameve.com

 **Ultimate Personal Shaver**... Surprise your lover! Shaving shows more skin in your sexiest area – and now there's a new, easy way to get the look you'll both love! The Ultimate Personal Shaving System is a great idea! www.adameve.com

 **Be My Lover Kit**... imagine you and your lover sharing a pleasurable session of lovemaking... in a whole new way! It has edible warming oil, stimulating lubricant, inviting massage oil, and sensual, rich body butter filled with tropical oils and moisturizing vitamins! This love kit has all the sensual goodies you'll need for night after night of exhilarating intimacy! www.adameve.com

 Shaving Basket... includes the Dare To Bare DVD, Personal Shaver, Coochie Shaving Cream, Shaving Templates, Powder Brush, Shaving Baby Powder. www.holisticwisdom.com

Dare To Bare DVD... gives you tips on essential tools and techniques for safe and sensual experimentation. You'll also discover the best positions for getting turned on in the process. Watch as lovers demonstrate how physical contact becomes more intimate and more pleasurable on deliciously smooth skin. Let these five real couples show you how the art of sensual shaving can lead to wonderful erotic encounters. Watch and learn. Dare to Bare opens the door to a private playground for you and your partner. It's all here - the creative ideas, the explicit techniques, and the permission - guaranteed to improve a couple's sexual pleasure and lovemaking skills. www.holisticwisdom.com

Sexy Places to Shop All-Around-the-Town:

In your city or somewhere in your town, there are numerous shops that will cater to your seductive, romantic, erotic or fetish whims so take an afternoon off for some sexy shopping and have a better Tonight!

 Victoria's Secret Shops: this sexy-sweet shop angles more toward Romance, than Lust. It sells the complete romance package from the prettiest panties, lovely bras and sexy half-slips, to the sweetest smelling candles, bath gels, massage lotions, body powders, drawer sachets and perfumes.

 Frederick's Of Hollywood Shops: this sexy shop forgoes Romance and is always, always about the Lust! FOH sells everything naughty from Fantasy-Wear costumes, crotch-less panties and garters, marabou feather boas, lacy see-through panties, nipple-exposing bras to wigs, body jewelry and body glitters. It carries lingerie sizes up-to 3X, and sexy shoes and boots up-to size 12.

Spencer's Gifts Stores: this naughty shop sexy-sells it all from the extremely raunchy to the fun and experiential. Hot-blow oils, latex fanny-paddles, board games for lovers, sexual-play books, sticky tittie pasties, fuck-party packs from the Lover's Doctor Kit to Footie Fetish, boxed Fantasy-Wear, really nasty greeting cards, and crass sexual novelty items. Great store because it is always conveniently at a mall near you!

 **The Bath And Body Works**: if you want to plan a truly romantic evening, this shop is the best place to go. It features specialty-item bath powders, gels, bubbles, oils, beads and crystals, scented candles and soaps, edible massage creams and oils; cuddly robes and slippers, thick and plush bath towels, chunky bath sponges and soft back brushes, and many items to give him a lovely massage.

 **Local Adult Toy Stores**: I enjoy these types of stores because they are so much fun and there are things for sale that, in your wildest imagination, you never thought existed! Hometown Adult toy/bookstores in the USA outnumber McDonald's Restaurants by a 3-to-1 margin so get out of your house and go find one near you. The worst that can happen is that your inner-thighs will be really, really sore from too much fucking.

 **Home-Thrown Bad-Girl Parties**: my good friend, Renee, owns the site www.Partygals.com, which is one of the finest online companies that cater to women who want to throw private parties to sell sexual-girly things for clandestine bedroom fun. These intimate parties that are thrown in private homes, for you and your gal-pals or for couples parties.

Explore these sites: www.surpriseparties.com, www.fantasiahomeparties.com, www.passonparties.com, www.slumberparties.com or www.blisspartiesinc.com, and pick the in-home sex party that works for you. All of these in-home sex parties are designed to introduce you to the opportunity to remove the blah out of your romantic relationship. So, go to one of these parties or throw one yourself!

Sexy Places to Shop Online

Thanks to the World Wide Web, a girl can privately and shamelessly shop at the raunchiest and most imaginative sex stores on the Planet.

Listed below, are sexy web shops that I have compiled for your risqué shopping pleasure, and these stores are the very best in the business. Not only will you discover products that you never knew existed, you will also find products in your size, color and preference. Your choices always arrive in discreet, non-descript packaging so unsuspicious your Momma won't even question the box.

But before you hit that Send button to purchase any product, do shop around. You can comparison shop as easily as hitting a few keys on your keyboard, and you will find that it is worth the time and effort to get what you want at the lowest price.

All of the photographs featured in this chapter, are of the sexually-brilliant products you can purchase at www.adameve.com and www.babeland.com, and these online stores, as well as every one of the sexy-shopping sites listed below, want your business so check them all out and find the ones that work for you!

Best USA Internet Sex Stores:

www.adameve.com
www.babeland.com
www.evesgarden.com
www.adulttoychest.com
www.goodvibrations.com
www.store.playboy.com
www.Xandria.com
www.kinglove.com
www.pabo.com
www.blowfish.com
www.adultsupermart.com
www.sportsheets.com
www.liberatorshapes.com
www.ashleysextoys.com
www.Partygals.com
www.edenfantasys.com
www.clone-a-willy.com
www.carlton.com
www.avacadell.com
www.holisticwisdom.com
www.docjohnson.com
www.dearlady.com
www.spicygear.com
www.mypleasure.com
www.passionshops.com
www.iysextoys.com
www.myprivatetoybox.com
www.adultdvdgold.com
www.toyssexshop.com
www.salon.com
www.stockroom.com
www.pleasurenight.com
www.luckysextoys.com
www.Fn-Fun.Com
www.exalte.com
www.seekingo.com
www.intimatesynergy.com
www.drlust.com
www.drsusanblock.com
www.naughtynovelty.zoovy.com
www.sinfulplaythings.com
www.sediva.com
www.eroticshopping.com
www.censoredtoys.com
www.chocolatefantasies.com
www.plumparty.com

www.electriqueboutique.com
www.all-of-sex.com
www.forbiddenerotics.com
www.candleLighttoys.com
www.tantra-sex.com
www.lustique.com
www.cyberskinsextoys.com
www.kamashop.com

Best Overseas Internet Sex Stores:

www.satisfactiondirect.co.uk
www.loversemporium.co.uk
www.keepitkinky.co.uk
www.sextoys.co.uk

Best Worldwide Lingerie Web Stores:

www.trashy.com (United States)
www.victoriassecret.com (United States)
www.fredericks.com (United States)
www.montenapoleone.com (United States)
www.laperla.com (Italy)
www.viamontenapoleone.org (Italy)
www.arsrosa.com (Italy)
www.sabbiarosa.com (France)
www.bellaluxuries.com (France)
www.dreamdresser.com (Britain)
www.sexy-lingerie.uk.com (Britain)
www.agentprovocateur.com (Britain)
www.spoylt.com (Britain)

Specialty Chick Web Sites:

www.simplyshe.com
www.goddesslife.com
www.early2bed.com
www.athenainstitute.com
www.candycare.com
www.girlshop.com
www.mightyflirt.com
www.bodyperks.com
www.curliegirl.com

Gourmet Food Sites:

www.macys.com
www.paramountcaviar.com
www.autumn-harvest.com
www.steelsgourmet.com
www.goodfood2u.com
www. harryanddavid.com

www.epicureanfoods.com
www.cajun-gifts.com
www.ffgc.com
www.wvgourmetfoods.com
www.caviaretc.com
www.annasgourmet.com
www.purelyamerican.com
www.intlgourmet.com
www.winecountrygiftbaskets.com
www.pancakeshop.com
www.delightfuldeliveries.com
www.beercollections.com
www.articochef.com
www.fantasiahomeparties.com
www.passonparties.com
www.slumberparties.com
www.blisspartiesinc.com

What you've seen and read in this chapter isn't even the tip-of-the-sex-you-can-get-iceberg. There is *so much* more out there for you to explore, touch, see and experience *so please do*.

You can have the romantic relationship dreamed about and written about in all of your little girl fantasies and fairytales. All it takes is real effort, imagination and determination; and isn't that much easier than getting your prince because you were cursed asleep for one hundred years, or because you ate a poisoned apple!

goddesspornstardivagoddesspornstardivagoddesspornstardivagoddessp
ornstardivagoddesspornstardivagoddesspornstardivagoddesspornstard
ivagoddesspornstardivagoddesspornstardivagoddesspornstardivagodde
sspornstardivagoddesspornstardivagoddesspornstardivagoddesspornst
ardivagoddesspornstardivagoddesspornstardivagoddesspornstardivago
ddesspornstardivagoddesspornstardivagoddesspornstardivagoddesspor
nstardivagoddesspornstardivagoddesspornstardivagoddesspornstardiv
agoddesspornstardivagoddesspornstardivagoddesspornstardivagoddess
pornstardivagoddesspornstardivagoddesspornstardivagoddesspornstar
divagoddesspornstardivagoddesspornstardivagoddesspornstardivagodd
esspornstardivagoddesspornstardivagoddesspornstardivagoddesssporns
tardivagoddesspornstardivagoddesspornstardivagoddesspornstardivag
oddesspornstardivagoddesspornstardivagoddesspornstardivagoddessppo
rnstardivagoddesspornstardivagoddesspornstardivagoddesspornstardi
vagoddesspornstardivagoddesspornstardivagoddesspornstardivagoddes

Private Dancer

spornstardivagoddesspornstardivagoddesspornstardivagoddesspornsta
rdivagoddesspornstardivagoddesspornstardivagoddesspornstardivagod
desspornstardivagoddesspornstardivagoddesspornstardivagoddesssporn
stardivagoddesspornstardivagoddesspornstardivagoddesspornstardiva
goddesspornstardivagoddesspornstardivagoddesspornstardivagoddessp
ornstardivagoddesspornstardivagoddesspornstardivagoddesspornstard
ivagoddesspornstardivagoddesspornstardivagoddesspornstardivagodde
sspornstardivagoddesspornstardivagoddesspornstardivagoddesspornst
ardivagoddesspornstardivagoddesspornstardivagoddesspornstardivago
ddesspornstardivagoddesspornstardivagoddesspornstardivagoddesspor
nstardivagoddesspornstardivagoddesspornstardivagoddesspornstardiv
agoddesspornstardivagoddesspornstardivagoddesspornstardivagoddess
pornstardivagoddesspornstardivagoddesspornstardivagoddesspornstar
divagoddesspornstardivagoddesspornstardivagoddesspornstardivagodd
esspornstardivagoddesspornstardivagoddesspornstardivagoddesssporns
tardivagoddesspornstardivagoddesspornstardivagoddesspornstardivag
oddesspornstardivagoddesspornstardivagoddesspornstardivagoddessppo
rnstardivagoddesspornstardivagoddesspornstardivagoddesspornstardi
vagoddesspornstardivagoddesspornstardivagoddesspornstardivagoddes
spornstardivagoddesspornstardivagoddesspornstardivagoddesspornsta
rdivagoddesspornstardivagoddesspornstardivagoddesspornstardivagod
desspornstardivagoddesspornstardivagoddesspornstardivagoddesssporn
stardivagoddesspornstardivagoddesspornstardivagoddesspornstardiva
goddesspornstardivagoddesspornstardivagoddesspornstardivagoddessp
ornstardivagoddesspornstardivagoddesspornstardivagoddesspornstard
ivagoddesspornstardivagoddesspornstardivagoddesspornstardivagodde
sspornstardivagoddesspornstardivagoddesspornstardivagoddesspornst
ardivagoddesspornstardivagoddesspornstardivagoddesspornstardivago
ddesspornstardivagoddesspornstardivagoddesspornstardivagoddesspor
nstardivagoddesspornstardivagoddesspornstardivagoddesspornstardiv
agoddesspornstardivagoddesspornstardivagoddesspornstardivagoddess
pornstardivagoddesspornstardivagoddesspornstardivagoddesspornstar
divagoddesspornstardivagoddesspornstardivagoddesspornstardivagodd
esspornstardivagoddesspornstardivagoddesspornstardivagoddesssporns
tardivagoddesspornstardivagoddesspornstardivagoddesspornstardivag
oddesspornstardivagoddesspornstardivagoddesspornstardivagoddessppo
rnstardivagoddesspornstardivagoddesspornstardivagoddesspornstardi
vagoddesspornstardivagoddesspornstardivagoddesspornstardivagoddes
spornstardivagoddesspornstardivagoddesspornstardivagoddesspornsta
rdivagoddesspornstardivagoddesspornstardivagoddesspornstardivagod
desspornstardivagoddesspornstardivagoddesspornstardivagoddesssporn

XIV. Private Dancer

One of the greatest secrets of Eastern books of love is that sex offers rewards deeper than pure physical love and emotional pleasure. It can heal, and offer a gateway of spiritual ecstasy... sex is approached as a sacrament act, a gift from the gods to be treated with reverence and respect... in this holistic view of lovemaking, the power of sexual energy brings mind, body and spirit into harmony.

~~~Michelle Pauli in 'Sex Secrets'

Woman's desire to remain romantic, giving, sensual, sexy... and continue in her romantic relationship to do all that she did to 'get her man'... wilt and eventually disintegrate as the relationship progresses into deeper commitment.

Rather than directing Woman to a better understanding of her sexuality and showing Woman that she is independent and equal to Man, and that by remaining romantic and sensual with and toward her man she has The Power and The Glue that keeps her romantic relationship intact, Woman is continually brainwashed by those of her own sex into believing that she must be a hard-hearted vixen to get positive results in a pro-male society.

You already know of what I am speaking.

How many times has a girlfriend, a co-worker, your neighbor or your mother told you that it is not your place to take care of your man... and that he is the one that should take care of you?

I am a very free-thinking and independent woman, and along with that comes the fact that I have a very outgoing and forceful personality. I discovered long ago the power of subservience to a man within the confines of sweet romance and in the giving of sexual pleasure. Having learned these things, I have been able to maintain balance in a romantic relationship while being a sexual entity, and while remaining wholly myself.

The art of romance and the ingenuity to take sex to new and untraveled heights will always come from you... it will rarely, if ever, come from your man.

Your man's romantic and sexual mentality is actually very limited to buying flowers or to what sex acts he'd see on any porn site or DVD... so trust me when I tell you that you have a romantic and carnal imagination that far surpasses your man's, and access to this privileged status allows you the ability to adore and seduce your man far and beyond what limited emotive or sexual fantasies he possesses.

This chapter is far-reaching in ideas and information, from the sacredly sexual to the ingeniously romantic, and I've researched and gathered this information from every available source. You will have access to whatever you need to completely renovate your sexual and romantic relationship... and to take your man to an attainable plateau where the physical meets the emotional, mental and spiritual - to give your man a Completeness that can come only from you.

The Sex Goddess

Creative Intercourses

1) **Palm Intercourse**: Wet your palms with Kama Sutra Sweet Almond Oil. Cup your hands together, interlock your fingers and cross your thumbs. This will create a small opening between your thumbs and second fingers and the fusion of your palms to your little fingers will create a closure. Use the muscles between your thumbs and second finger to apply vaginal-like pressure to his cock.

2) **Sole Intercourse**: Lay a blanket on the floor and drench the soles of your feet with Kama Sutra Sweet Almond Oil. Lie on your back or sit-up straight. Bend your legs and then bow them to your own point-of-comfort, with your feet touching toes-to-toes, heels-to-heels, propped on a pillow. Have him straddle you with his back to you, and hunch down until his cock is between your feet and his ass is resting on your legs. As he begins to move his cock between your feet, gently slide your feet into the X-position, with one heel resting over the other.

3) **Innerthigh Intercourse**: Splash your inner-thighs with Kama Sutra Sweet Almond Oil. Bend over and lean forward until the upper part of your body is horizontal and your legs are vertical. You can press your hands against a wall or hold-on to a chair or the edge of the bed. He'll come-up behind you, his hands on your hips and his cock will slide between your oil-soaked thighs. Inner Thigh Intercourse can also be done while you lie on your side and as he lays beside you... and it is a great substitution when you have your period or are in your last months of pregnancy.

4) **Breast Intercourse**: Sop your breasts with Kama Sutra Sweet Almond Oil. Lie back, sit up or sit upright between his legs while he straddles you, either at the edge of the bed or on a comfortable chair, where he can easily slide his cock between your breasts. If you are smaller breasted you can either press your breasts together with your hands or try this: 1) have him lay on his back with his legs bent at the knees and spread wide. 2) Move your body

between his spread legs, take his cock and lean it against one of his thighs. 3) Press your cleavage into his cock and move from slide-to-slide or in slow, circular motions until the combined frictions makes him cum.

5) **Knee-Fold Intercourse**: Splash back-of-knees with Kama Sutra Sweet Almond Oil. Lie on your back or your side and bed both your knees. You man will knee upright or lie against you, with his body his feet to your head, and push his cock between the oiled folds of your oiled inner knees. Knee-Fold Intercourse is a great substitution when you've got your period or are in the last months of pregnancy.

6) **Axillary Intercourse**: Douse your armpit with Kama Sutra Sweet Almond Oil. Lie either on your side, your back or sit upright. Position his body until his cock can slide comfortably between your underarm.

7) **Innerarm Intercourse**: Soak the bend of either arm with Kama Sutra Sweet Almond Oil. Lie back, sit or even stand, and glide his cock in, then bend your arm upwards. His cock will easily slide inside your forearm.

Sex Goddess Manuals and Accessories

From the glorious website www.kama-sutra-free.com, you will find all the Sensual Knowledge you need to give your man Goddess Sex... just as it was given to men hundreds of years ago when the Act of Sex was a thing of emotional beauty and expression for a woman in love, and not an act of 'have-too' or 'a job.'

www.kama-sutra-free.com, gives you every version of Goddess Sex though Romantic Love. Besides written explanations of these Asian and Indian expressions of love, this website visually shows you, by using doll-models, each sacred sexual position from The Kama Sutra, Ananga Ranga, The Perfumed Garden and The Tao.

A true Sex Goddess needs these manuals in her lusty repertoire.

The Manuals

Written around 1172 AD the Ananga Ranga was specifically aimed at preventing the separation of husband and wife. The Author Kalyana Malla says: "The chief reason for the *separation between the married couple and the cause which drives the husband to the embraces of strange women, and the wife to the embraces of strange men, is the want of varied pleasures, and the monotony which follows possession. The Ananga Ranga was actually a collection of erotic works and includes sections from the Kama Sutra.*"

"The Perfumed Garden was written by Sheikh Nefzawi in the late 15th century. At the time, the culture in North Africa was quite male dominated. The Perfumed Garden was something that was to be hidden from women. Needless to say the text provided advice for how men could receive great pleasure. Unfortunately it barely touched on the woman's experience."

"The Tao is a collection of ancient Chinese wisdom. It predates the Kama Sutra, The Perfumed Garden, and the Ananga Ranga. Taoists believe that sex and sexual energy can be used to improve health, harmonize relationships, and increase spiritual realization. Many of the Tao sexual positions are recommended to promote the flow of sexual health and energy. It is obvious from the visual names given to Tao positions that the Chinese viewed sex as an art form."

"The Kama Sutra has been a source of great mystery and excitement for lovers seeking sexual adventure. Kama Sutra is Sanskrit (an ancient Hindu language) for Desire Rules. It is the earliest and best known Indian sex manual. It was written by an Indian sage, Vatsyayana, between the 1st and 4th Centuries AD. Then it was translated into English by the 19th Century British explorer, Sir Richard F. Burton, in 1876. With each translation, the Kama

Sutra's contents have become more distorted, so I would like to give you the explanation of the original Kama Sutra. The Kama Sutra is renowned for its creative sexual positions, a total of 64 that Vatsyayana derived from eight ways of making love, multiplied by eight positions."

This entire Narration taken From: www.avacadell.com

Ava knows her Kama Sutra---please visit her site!
(more on Ava Cadell later in this chapter)

The Accessories

 **The Spinning Sex Swing**... this is an incredible piece of hardware that no couple should be without... so enjoy all the positions of the Kama Sutra! Consisting of a heavily padded back support, rear support and stirrups, the spinning sex swing gives you the additional freedom of 360 degree rotation! Use your imagination, consult the Kama Sutra book or look at the photos on the box. You'll never run out of uses for this incredible swing! It comes with a spring, instruction booklet and all hardware for mounting. Swing holds up to 200 lbs. with the spring in place or 400 lbs without the spring. www.chocolatefantasies.com

Kama Sutra Spinner Game... a sensual and sexual game of closeness and intimacy for lovers to discover the joys and pleasures of each other. There are three circles and a spinner that create the activity. The passive partner will spin the spinner three times. The first spin is for the outside circle and is the part of the active player's body that will be doing the pleasuring. The second spin is for the middle circle and is the part of the passive partner's body that will receive the pleasuring. The last spin is for the inner circle and is the type of pleasuring the active player will use to pleasure their partner. www.chocolatefantasies.com

Kama Sutra Lubricants... Love Liquid - Newly designed with the sensitive tissues of a woman in mind, this silky water-based lubricant is formulated without sugars. Smooth and slippery, this unscented moisturizing lubricant is a love making essential. Brahma - This new thick, highly concentrated water-based gel is formulated to provide pleasing friction. Its no-drip long lasting smoothness will give hours of pleasure. Pleasure Potion - This new long lasting silicone based lubricant provides unlimited hours of passion. Silky and never sticky. Pleasure Potion is the standard others will be measured by. Royal Bengal - This ultra-rich and highly concentrated new silicone lubricant is simply luxurious. Royal Bengal was created for those who demand the very best. It has a classy container design with a convenient flip cap on all bottle sizes. Remember to never use silicone based lubricants with silicone toys. www.chocolatefantasies.com

Tantra Sex by Ava Cadell

Dr. Ava Cadell is an accomplished author of seven books and she is a Love Guru, Media Therapist and World Class Speaker who has appeared on numerous national shows including Good Morning America, CNN, MSNBC, NBC, ABC & Fox News, and she has done a variety of shows for MTV, VH1, Discovery, Lifetime, Learning Channel. Due to her expertise, Dr. Ava has been named by the media as the Martha Stewart of Love and Intimacy. Dr. Ava's mission is to promote the benefits of healthy love and intimacy to individuals and couples around the globe.

The following information on Tantric Sex, has been taken from Dr. Ava's website www.avacadell.com I encourage you to go to Dr. Ava's website and seek out her sexual and emotive wisdom. Dr. Ava also offers one of the best online stores for products that will cater to your romantic relationship... physically, mentally, emotionally and spiritually. www.avacadell.com

Dr. Ava's Intro to Tantra

"Many people are unclear about what Tantra is and what it is not. Tantra is not a religion, a sexual cult, a new age spiritual philosophy, exhibitionism, swinging or sex therapy. Tantra is a Sanskrit (ancient Hindu language) word that means to weave energy, specifically Yin (female) and Yang (male) energy between two lovers. This energy includes our thoughts, feelings, physical and sexual actions. There are several different kinds of Tantra, but we are going to focus on Red Tantra, which directs sexual energy to your lover. So I'd like to welcome you to a unique journey of sensual and sexual exploration that will prepare you for the 5,000 year old practice of Tantra.

Tantra can help to heal a hurt relationship; it can break down defensive walls, improve intimate communication and enhance a relationship that has lost its sizzle and spice. For women, Tantra can empower and fulfill their sensual needs, for men it can open up a whole new world to intimacy and it can give them the tools to become multi-orgasmic. For couples it's an opportunity to create a more meaningful and intimate connection. So, get ready to explore new sexual territory, expand your ideas about your relationship, intimacy and sex.

To do this you will need to learn and experience all six of the essential Tantric elements; Breath, Movement, Muscle Lock, Sound, Intention and Attention and to enjoy the journey of Tantra, rather than focusing on your immediate pleasure (climax). Achieving Tantric Bliss through the six elements of Tantra will take your relationship to a whole new physical, emotional and spiritual level. Here's an opportunity for you to enjoy the quest for enlightenment together and become one with the Universe!"

~~~Dr. Ava Cadell

Dr. Ava's Tantra Kissing

"A kiss can be one of the most erotic exchanges between lovers. A kiss is often the first intimate physical contact with a new lover and some people believe they can tell a lot about a person's lovemaking skills by the way they kiss. Some people can reach orgasm through kissing alone. Not wanting to be kissed by your partner is a signal of trouble in the relationship. Making kissing a daily ritual will embolden and re-ignite passion in your relationship and it will keep the juices flowing. There are many different kinds of kisses: slow, quick, deep, wet, hard, soft, breathy, and then there is Tantric kissing. Kiss your lover at least twice a day and experiment with the different kinds of kisses from below:

• Eye brow kissing: Face your lover in Yab-Yum position, either woman on top or man on top, moisten each other's eyebrows and then lean into each other with brows touching. Feel the energy flow from one to the other uniting the two of you into a higher level of consciousness.

• Synchronized kissing: Embrace in your favorite lovemaking position with lingam and yoni touching, but not inserted. Lips slightly open and touching as you both inhale together gently and exhale together, sharing and synchronizing the same breath.

• Orgasmic kissing: In a loving face-to-face intercourse position with lingam inserted into yoni, lock lips, eye-gaze and one person inhales as the other person exhales, then the other exhales while the other inhales. Share the deep level of intimacy and feel your lover's sexual breath enter your body and spirit."

~~~Dr. Ava Cadell

www.avacadell.com

174

Dr. Ava's Tantric Sex Games for Lovers

"Tantra is a Sanskrit word that means to weave energy, specifically Yin (female) and Yang (male) energy between two lovers. This energy includes our thoughts, feelings, physical and sexual actions. I'd like to welcome you to a unique journey of sensual and sexual exploration that will prepare you for the 5000 year old practice of Tantra.

Tantra can improve intimate communication and enhance a relationship that has lost its sizzle and spice. For women, Tantra can empower and fulfill their sensual needs, for men it can open up a whole new world to intimacy. For couples it's an opportunity to create a more meaningful, intimate and spiritual connection. This is an ancient form of worshipping and loving each other. So, get ready to explore new sexual territory with the following Tantric sexercises.

First you need to prepare a few props to make your Tantra experience even more memorable and magical. Find a scarf that you can use as a blindfold to take away one of your lovers senses. Make sure you have some massage oil, water based lubricant and last but not least some feathers, big or small will complete your prop list.

The following Tantric sexercises are all about enjoying the journey of sensuality as opposed to the destination of orgasm.

1. Striptease:

Take turns taking off three pieces of your clothing for your lover slowly and provocatively. Add music so that you move your body to the rhythm.

2. Symphony:

Imagine you are a musician, choose an instrument, and play a rhythm on your lover's naked body for at least five minutes. Your lover has to guess what kind of musician you are and what you are playing, then alternate.

3. Surrender:

Surrender yourself to your lover and let him/her caresses and kiss you wherever he/she wants for five minutes then alternate. Use a blindfold and even restraints.

4. Tantric Breath:

Blow your warm breath all over your lover's naked body from their neck to their toes, both sides and then alternate. You can also use a feather to tickle one part of their body while you are blowing your warm breath on another part.

5. Finger Walking:

Walk your fingers over your own body and show your lover five places that excite you the most for at least five minutes. Then ask your lover to show you what they have learned. And alternate.

6. Tantric Kiss:

Bend over your lover and kiss all around his/her face with baby kisses and use your hands to caress him/her simultaneously. Then trace your lover's lips with your tongue, take your lover's bottom lip between yours and suck gently, suck on your lover's tongue with your lips and end in a passionate, wet, smoldering Tantric kiss for at least five minutes.

7. Tantric Dance:

Stand and hold each other close and move your bodies together, swaying from side to side, rolling your hips and grinding your pelvises into each other without moving your feet. Add some sexy music to enhance your movements."

~~~Dr. Ava Cadell

www.avacadell.com

Creative Screwing Sex-Specialties

These incredible moves do take practice... but once you've perfected them, any one will of them will give your man innovative and unbelievable mind-altering sex.

Because you will not be able to pull-off these Sex-Specialties the first few times you try them, you may want to practice on a cock-shaped dildo or a cock-shaped vibrator, so you can get it right quicker.

Treat your body, and that of your lover, as a temple, and lovemaking becomes an act of worship.

~~~Michelle Pauli, in 'Spiritual Sex'

Repose(relaxation)Intercourse:

1. Lie down on large cushion, a fur rug, or a bed with satin or silk sheets.

2. Have your man lie on top of you in the Missionary Position, and once his cock is deep inside you, ask him to lay motionless.

3. Bring your legs up, and press your knees against the sides of his body.

4. There need be very little mobility of your inner vaginal muscles as you gently pump those muscles around his cock. You can then begin to sway your hips in a slow and tedious motion.

5. As he lies still on top of you, run your fingertips along his body and play with his hair, touching him very lightly.

6. Close your eyes, sink your fingers into his hair and move your inner-vaginal muscles clockwise as you pump and clench those muscles around his cock, sucking him further in.

7. His orgasm, as well as yours, will feel very different from the hard thrust of regular intercourse... because the sluggish movement will leave you both experiencing a unique kind of orgasmic exhaustion.

Karezza Intercourse:

1. You will have total control of any and all his movements.

2. Lie on your back.

3. When his cock is in your pussy, tell him to take only three deep strokes.

4. After he stops, re-build the tension with your vaginal muscles by the suck-clench movement five times, *but do not* move your hips or your body in anyway.

5. After the fifth suck-clench, tell him to take another three deep strokes.

6. After he's stopped, repeat your five suck-clench moves.

7. This takes a lot of practice, but if you can get him to the 10th Round, when he finally cums, it will literally make him dizzy and knock him senseless. You'll need to make sure he's well-rested before getting out of bed.

Slow Masturbation:

Historians have written that Rulers and Kings paid high prices for concubines skilled in this Sex-Specialty.

1. Lay him back on soft cushions, a fur rug or on your bed with satin or silk sheets.

2. Take his legs and bend them, crossing them at the ankles and gently tying them with a cloth or any type of soft material until his ankles ate secure.

3. Take both his arms up over his head and tie his wrists gently behind his head so that his head will lean on his wrists, as if he were lying with his hands behind his head at the beach.

4. Sit upright on his chest with your back to him, your ass slid to his chin, your feet tucked under each of his shoulders. Begin to kiss his tummy area and all around his cock, but do not kiss his cock.

5. Lean forward, oil-up your hands with Kama Sutra Sweet Almond Oil, and starting at the very tip of his cock, oil him all the way down his cock-shaft to the base.

6. Slide your left-hand down the shaft and pull the skin on his cock downward until it bundles to the end-of-his-shaft, leaving the shaft tight and taunt.

7. As your left-hand holds his shaft tight, use your right-hand to stroke his cock with quick and even movements, fifteen-times. Stop, count to ten and repeat again, this time, stroking him ten-times. Stop again, count to ten and repeat from fifteen. *Perform this exercise five times; ten if he can take it.*

8. After you've made the last fifteen strokes, use your right hand to release the bonds on his feet and then quickly pump his cock until he cums. He will want to release his hands, but because they are bound he will be unable to do so, and that frustration will cause him to cum harder then he'll anticipate.

9. After he's cum and you've released his hands, make sure you get him a beer or a soda or water, because he will be exhausted and a little dehydrated from this Sex Goddess move. If it's a hot day, put a fan on him and if it's a cold day, cuddle him up in a cozy blanket.

Silken Oral Ecstasy:

This oral technique is from the Orient and young Oriental woman are taught this seductive move before marriage. Asian Concubines who prove exceptional at this Sex Goddess move acquire a very high price for their service.

1. Lay him back on soft cushions, a fur rug, or on a bed with silk or satin sheets.

2. Once he's on his back, bend him at the knees then bow his legs out, where one knee faces East and the other knee faces West.

3. Take a thick yarn and securely tie his ankles. You must use *only yarn* for this specialty, because you will need to

quickly slice the yarn at the Precise Moment with a scissors or a knife.

4. Once his ankles are tied, straddle him with your back and buttocks aligned for his visual. I suggest you make sure that his neck is comfortably placed with a neck pillow, and for this move, that you choose between two scenes 1) An assortment of scented candles for light, with seductive background music. 2) Lights completely out (with exception of a small light for you down by his feet); his favorite porn movie in the DVD player where he can watch as you perform on him.

5. This move requires a lot of lubricant so you'll need an edible sex oil or sex lube. Once his cock is fully oiled or lubed-up and you've made sure his ankles are securely tied (you need to make sure his feet are securely tied because he will want to move his legs once you get started) begin to suck his cock using any of the Great Head moves in the chapter 'Nuclear Head'.

6. When he starts to cum, begin to suck his cock harder and, just as he blows cum, reach for the scissors and slice the yarn that restrains his ankles.

7. I like to follow this move with a full, light body massage. It will put your man right to sleep.

Abyssiania Holder:

The Kama Sutra of India read that any woman who does this to her man is "... loved above all women" and that her man is "... the envy of all his friends."

1. Lie him back, flat on a bed with satin or silk sheets, his head resting on the bed without a pillow.

2. Spread-eagle his legs.

3. Move your body over his, with your knees bent and resting against his hip bones.

4. Slide his cock inside you.

5. Sit straight and up-right, with his cock deep inside your pussy, then grasp his kneecaps with your hands and lock your arms straight at your elbows.

6. *Be still.* Make no bodily movement what-so-ever and as you keep your body still and do not allow him to move his cock inside of you.

7. Begin to pump your vaginal and pelvic muscles around his cock, to the count of fifty.

8. Release your arms and gently slide your hips upward and move your body forward until *only* the tip of his cock is inside your pussy. Slide your hands to his ankles and grasp them tight, and begin to suck-and-pump the head of his cock until you have milked-out his cum.

Your Sexual Signature

Your man's sexual memories are nothing more-than a haze of every woman he's ever been with; unless a woman had a sexual signature that was so intense it put a twist and a knot in his sexual-memory-wiring so that he still masturbates about it and remembers it every single time he has sex with another woman. Like Cosmopolitan puts it: *"A woman's sexual signature is the difference between sex that's Gold-Medal Memorable or yellow-light forgettable."*

A man's brain is connected to his cock the exact same way that wires are connected in an electronic device. Because of this sweet Fact, you can give your man a sex session that is so sacred he will sub-consciously reach for it every time that he is away from you.

One client who wrote to me for advice wanted something really special and memorable that she could do for her lover on his birthday... so I emailed her Sacred Sensual Sex. A few months later she emailed me again, depressed and unhappy because he'd broken-up with her. I advised her to just sit back and wait, because the private things she'd done to him and with him sexually were planted deep within his sub-conscience and that eventually, it would all surface. Another three months went by, and my client emailed me yet again, this time to tell me that her ex wanted to get back together and that he'd told her the sex he'd had with other women after he dated her always left him feeling more unsatisfied than not having sex at all.

What you do to your man and with your man sexually, matters so much more than you've ever stopped to consider. Hundreds of books have been written that back this Fact up, yet women continue to ignore and reject the obvious... and then wonder why men have affairs or aren't as romantic or as attentive as they used to be in a romantic relationship.

Having seen one's partner as a god or goddess,
one naturally feels a sense of devotion.
At this point there is no need for elaborate instructions,
as love play spontaneously becomes a sport of deities.
Every gesture becomes an act of worship, every sigh and
word of love becomes a prayer, and gazing into the lovers;
eyes become a one-pointed meditation.

~~~Miranda Shaw

The most powerful woman in the world is his Sex Goddess, his Kissing Queen, and his Private Porn Star.

Believe it.

The Sacred Sex Ceremony

The Sacred Sex Ceremony is a ritual in which your man will be totally receptive and you will be totally in control. What you do in the Scared Sex Ceremony for your man, will bring him to a sexual-place he has never before traveled. Most men do not recognize the Spiritual side of sex because it has never been shown to them. This is your opportunity to show your man just how sweet It is.

Listen Peaceful Warrior... By: Ishtara

Come here and relax

let the eternal feminine hold you tenderly

Come and penetrate softly
The fountains of silence
And rest in the depth
Of her golden cavern.

The return to innocence,
To the eternal womb of creation.
Let her hold you tenderly
While you be still and receive
The nectar of her inexhaustible passion

Relax
There is nothing to do
And nowhere to go
you've come here
To taste the ecstasy
That is your birthright.

www.sacredsexsecrets.com

You will begin with **The Bathing Ritual**, a hot sensual bubble bath to physically relax your man and to adjust him internally and converge his mind and his body for anticipated sexual pleasure.

The Bathing Ritual Set-Up: you will completely fill the bathtub making sure that the bubbles in the bath are frothy and plenty. For this, you must use a high-quality bubble bath. You will need a large, thick towel of high-quality grade and your only lighting should be a few well-place masculine-scented candles. You will also need relaxing background music on a small cd-player. On a small table or tray, set a glass of cold water, decaffeinated soda or beer. You can make him a mixed-drink if that's what he'd prefer. If you choose to do a **Sacred Sensual Sex Ceremony** in cooler months, hot tea, decaffeinated coffee, a rich, hot coco or a Hot Toddy are a good idea.

The Bathing Ritual: after you've helped your man step into the bath, use a good-quality, very fluffy-soft loofah-puff to gently wash his back and his chest. Use good quality masculine liquid body soap, and dunk the loofah-puff in the bath water first, so that you'll get a lot of suds. Massage his back, neck, arms, throat and chest with the loofah-puff in slow, circular motions. Gently lift each of his legs and one-at-a-time, run the loofah-puff from his feet to his thighs. Once you can see that his body is relaxed and pampered, you can begin to wash his hair. First, make sure that you have a bathing cup handy so that you can pour the bath-water onto his head. Next, as you begin to wash his hair, gently massage his scalp, using your finger tips to run interference from the base of his neck to his hairline on his forehead. If you have fingernails you can use them to gently scratch his head and his temple and behind his earlobes.

Next, you will do **The Sacred Sex Ceremony**: the world is fascinated with sex because as human beings it is in our Genetic Code to instinctively Know that sex is the All-Healer for the soul. This is why having sex with someone with whom we have a deep connection means so much more than casual sex with someone who does not know the worst, as well as the best, of who we are. When you touch and massage your man in such a private and intimate way, it will nurture his spirit and awaken his soul... because the vicinity of the male g-spot where his prostate gland lies is the active Access of Intention and Intensity which leads to his emotional enlightenment.

The Sacred Sexual Ceremony: you will begin with a gentle massage from your man's throat to his toes. Make sure that you have Kama Sutra Sweet Almond Oil for the massage, unscented baby wipes, and satin sheets for him to lie on. Because 99% of communication is non-verbal, make sure to use plenty of eye contact with him so that he can see from your eyes how much you adore him. After he is relaxed from the front massage, turn him over on his tummy and begin to massage him from his neck to his heels. After about fifteen minutes, take both your hands in a gentle sweeping motion to his buttocks. Using Kama Sutra Sweet Almond Massage Oil on your hands, take both your thumbs from the base of his buttocks and sweep them softly between the cheeks of his buttocks, slowly spreading them until you're right thumb is resting on the outer part of his anus. Slowly begin to massage him in steady, circular motions, putting pressure on the outside of his g-spot as he begins to moan. Continue to do this until he wants to stroke his cock for release. As he strokes his cock to orgasm, don't stop... continue to evenly massage his anus as he cums. Your man will experience a full body orgasm and a deep emotional release followed by immense pleasure... and the most important thing is that you will give your man a safe environment to feel and express his needs because you will have become his devoted healer: one that can escort and sustain him.

This is a loving, giving and spiritual experience that will be transform him physically, emotionally, mentally and spiritually... it will make you Unforgettable to him.

The Kissing Queen

1) Give your man kisses from his tummy to his inner thighs.

2) Kiss your man top-to-bottom, front-to-back, and side-to-side and explore his entire body.

3) Kiss his belly-button with wet kisses around his navel with use your tongue right in the button.

4) Softly lick his nipples with your tongue and suck-in the tip of his nipples with your lips.

5) Roll him over and literally kiss his ass, starting at his waist, and then doing an around-the-world from one of his sweet butt-cheeks to the other, kiss-kiss-kissing non-stop until he moans with glee.

6) Passionately kiss all around his lips and then nimbly suck and lightly lick the inside of his lips.

7) Take-His-Pout-Prisoner plan by Ava Cadell, Ph.D.:

a) Kiss your lover's face all over. Start `with dry, baby pecks on his eyebrows, chin, and cheeks.

b) Trace the outline of your lover's lips with the tip of your tongue. When you get to his mouth, don't dive in; instead, slowly exert a little more pressure.

c) Entice him by pulling back and sucking gently on his bottom lip.

d) Finally, go in for a kiss, this time with a lot of wetness to increase the sexual excitement and don't forget to use your hands in the make-out mission by caressing his hair, face, thighs, and buttocks.

8) Lick, kiss and nibble his earlobes. Another sweet move, is to kiss one of his ear lobes while you gently rub his other earlobe with your fingertips.

9) While he's driving in traffic or if he's really tense from a bad day, take one of his hands and press kisses and little teeth nibbles into the webbed-part between his thumb and his forefinger. It will send little tingles directly to his cock.

10) Take his bottom lip and gently suck it into your mouth while your hands caress his face. Then move your lips to the little hollow spot in his neck and kiss him there until he shivers with delight.

Massage Goddess

Michelle R. Kluck-Ebbin is *the* reigning queen of massage and reflexology. Michelle writes:

"The practice of massage dates back as early as 3000 B.C. In fact, a series of hieroglyphics were recently found in an ancient Egyptian tomb depicting two people rubbing each other's feet. Historically, Cleopatra's attentive lover, Marc Anthony, was accused (by Calsivius, one of his enemies) of massaging her feet during dinner parties. Then, of course, there's the Kama Sutra, the ancient Indian book of love that teaches couples the finer points of eroticism including massage. Sensual massage is an intimate and wonderful way for two people to communicate with each other through touch. The power to heal, relax, and infuse your sweetheart with loving energy is literally at your fingertips. Just follow the tips outlined below to create a romantic, loving evening that will surely provide a deeper level of intimacy for your loved one."

The Massage Preparation:

First, set the mood. Turn the lights down low and light candles scented with jasmine or vanilla. If you have a fireplace, use it, and treat the senses to the exotic smell of incense - a good one to use is Nag Champa, the Indian temple incense. Play sensual, relaxing atmospheric music in the background. Next, prepare your sensual treats. Before you begin massaging, rub something sweet on your sweetheart's lips. A taste of honey or a dab of chocolate sauce will whet your lover's appetite for amour.

The most important ingredient in massage is oil. Use massage oil scented with essential oils of lavender or chamomile for relaxation; musk, patchouli, or ylang-ylang to heighten ardor. But remember, a little oil goes a long way, so use only a light coat that will allow your hands to glide smoothly over the body without pulling on the skin.

Giving Him a Sensual Massage
by Michelle R. Kluck-Ebbin:

First, have your partner lie on his or her stomach, head turned to the side. Kneel at the head, and gently but firmly, glide your hands down the back (avoiding the bones of the spine), around the hips, and back up to the neck and shoulders. A good back massage will relax the whole body, but don't stop there if you're getting the hang of it. Move on to the arms and legs; always massaging these in an upward motion toward the heart. Spend extra time kneading and rubbing the parts of your partner's body he uses the most. If he is an athlete, give his legs extra attention. If he spends his days crouched in front of a computer, focus more on his neck and shoulders. In sensual massage, it's important to always maintain contact with your partner's body. When you need more oil, flip your hand over, so that the back of your hand is still touching your partner's body as you fill the palm of your hand with more oil.

Concentrate on smooth, slow strokes. Close your eyes, and envision healing white light coming out of your fingertips and being absorbed into your lover's skin. Think positive and loving thoughts about your partner, and you will soon begin to feel as though your hands and their body are melded together. Use your intuition and your partner's responses to guide your movements. Sensual massage is a tender expression of love that can energize the core of your soul. It is an experience that will not only heighten intimacy, but will provide for a deeper, more unified connection between you and the one you love. Remember, the soft should be touch and unless you are a certified massage therapist, don't apply too much pressure, rather, focus on the general sensation of touch.

Hands on Healing for your Man by Michelle R. Kluck-Ebbin:

For centuries, people all over the world have been using sensual massage to release tension, improve communication and develop a deeper, more meaningful relationship. As far back as three thousand years before the birth of Christ, records such as the Chinese "Nei Ching," as well as the Indian books of "Ayur Veda," written about 1800 B.C., and later, the "Kama Sutra," show that people recognized the therapeutic benefits of massage and used massage to heal each other. The Japanese, Romans and Greeks all believed in the power of massage: early Japanese literature by physicians makes reference to the benefits of massage, and Plato and Socrates refer often to the usefulness of massage. In Egypt, hieroglyphics dating back to 2300 B.C. were found in an ancient tomb depicting two people rubbing each other's feet. History talks about how.

It was said by Calsivius (a dependent of Gaius Julius Caesar) that Marc Anthony massaged Cleopatra's feet during dinner parties. Now wouldn't that be nice...

Sensual massage has been used for thousands of years to cure disease, preserve health and improve the overall state of well-being in mind and body. In addition to the many physical benefits, sensual massage is a wonderful way for two people to communicate with each other through touch and improve trust and understanding. It's a special kind of gift, a unique expression of yourself, your compassion and your love.

Show your man just how much you appreciate and care about him... draw on the power of your own healing, loving touch and with the gift of a sensual massage. Giving a massage is one of the sweetest ways of saying "I Love You."

1. First, create a romantic atmosphere: Dim the lights and light scented candles, maybe some incense. Turn on some soothing music you both enjoy and relax.

2. Make sure you have some massage oil so that you won't pull on the skin. Use oil scented with lavender or chamomile (relaxing) or musk or patchouli (sensual) for a soothing aromatherapy massage. A few minutes before the massage, warm the oil in the microwave for about 10 seconds. Warm oil feels very sexy on the skin.

3. Begin with a soothing back massage. Kneel at your man's head (he should be face down with head turned to the side) and glide your hands down the back, around the hips and back up the sides of the back and around the shoulders and neck. This is called an "effleurage" and it's a basic Swedish massage stroke. To get deeper into the muscles, lean your body weight forward as you glide your hands down the back. The leverage of your body weight and gravity will allow you to sink your hands deeper into tight muscles. Remember: Never massage directly on the spine but rather, on the muscles on either side of the spine.

4. Next, place your thumbs on either side of the spine (not on the spine itself) and glide your thumbs down the back. Lean forward as you move down the back, and try to keep your thumbs straight and the rest of your fingers relaxed. Imagine the energy coming out of your thumbs to loosen knots in the muscles. Repeat this again, this time stopping at various points to sink your thumbs in a little deeper. Using your thumbs like this is a technique of Acupressure which can open up the flow of energy in the back. This soothing back massage can relax your partner's entire body. These strokes can be used on all parts of the body.

5. Next, give your man a Reflexology Foot Massage. Begin by gently kneading one foot with both hands, using some oil or lotion. After a few minutes of kneading and relaxing the entire foot, you can focus on specific reflexology points on the foot. These reflex points correspond to various parts of the body and can affect the organ at the end of nerve. Use your thumbs to press gently on each area, making small circles for a few minutes.

If your man is interested, you can give great foot massages to each other at the same time. Sit on a couch facing each other and take one of his feet in your hands. As you massage each other's feet, you can look into each other's eyes and communicate without words, simply through your own loving touch.

Specialty Techniques by Michelle R. Kluck-Ebbin:

Ancient Massage, like most Asian methods, is a technique used to give mankind an experience of the total body. It is similar to acupressure and Shiatsu combined with stretches and yogic Asanas. Its nickname has become "yoga for the lazy." Ancient Massage will strengthen the client physically and harmonize their energy so a new life experience can arise.

Ancient Massage works on the major meridians, also called energy lines or Nadis, which run throughout the human body. It aims to harmonize the body, to loosen blocks, and to recoup deficiencies along the energy lines. In contrast to traditional Chinese medicine, which uses acupuncture to manipulate the pressure points, Ancient Massage stimulates these same points with healing touch. Therefore, the points suffer less stress, and life energy, or Prana, is allowed to freely circulate.

Along with influencing the energetic side, Ancient Massage also works on the physical body. Starting at the feet and progressing up to the head, his body will be moved, loosened and stretched. Ancient Massage combines techniques usually found isolated in the western physiotherapies including Trigger Point Treatments, Myofascial Techniques, Manual Therapy and others. The combination of energetic and physical aspects is unique to Ancient Massage, and so are its effects. Ancient Massage is a gift for the body, speech (energy) and mind (heart).

Ancient Massage is a way to prevent sickness. It will help your man to dissolve blocks before they manifest psychologically or physically, and it also improves flexibility. Injured athletes, as well as those suffering from

191

handicaps or stress are another target group. Essentially, your man will wholly benefit from this powerful technique.

Ancient Massage is a floor massage. Your man lies naked on a pad or light mattress. An ingenious system of movements allows you to manipulate your man without much effort. The massage is given in silence to allow you to understand your man and to give your man a chance to focus and learn about himself without distraction. To give and to experience Ancient Massage is a meditative practice. At the end of a two-hour treatment, both you and your man will feel relaxed and energized.

~~~Michelle R. Kluck-Ebbin

www.massage-tools.com is the best place on the Internet to find massage tools and equipment.

You can find all of Michelle R. Kluck-Ebbin's books in your local book store or online. She is an absolute expert and very well-trusted for her skill.

The Porn Star

Most women wonder what it would be like to be a porn star... it's a secret fantasy that licks at the fringes of that Good Girl/Bad Girl balance in our female DNA. I completely admit that if I were to choose a profession that would be considered risqué' or shocking... it would be a porn star. One of my best friend's says that she would be a bank robber. I love sex, she loves money... so the Bad-Girl chosen profession fits the personality!

You can become your man's Private Porn Star with a few fun, simple steps that will blow his mind. If you do this for him, I promise you that it will absolutely put the Hot-n-Spicy into a going-bland romantic relationship.

 **1. Get a Porn Star Name**... every porn star has an unusual name. Your first step is to find a name that would properly fit you. For terrific ideas on where to get the

perfect Porn Star Name, go to www.jasonschock.com, and put your real name into the *The Porn Star Name Generator*. When I put my real name into The Porn Star Name Generator, my Porn Star name came back as: *Kinky Slickbooty!* Another fantastic resource in finding your porn star name is to visit Yahoo's *Humorous Names Generators...* they have 20 sites which conjure up what your name would be if you were a Hobbit, A Jedi, a Hip Hop Queen or a Prison Bitch! When you hit the The Porn Star Name Generator, spend some time finding the perfect name that fits you. And while you're at it, put your man's name into the *Jedi* or *Military* or *Evangelist* Name Generators... and make that his 'John' Name.

2. Get Porn Star Gear... fuck-me-pumps, garish lipsticks, loud-flashy clothing and lingerie... that's just the tip-of-the-iceberg when it comes to Porn Star Gear... that's why it's a good idea to *choose a theme*. For instance: are you doing School Girl Porn or Biker Chick Porn? If you're going to be his School Girl, your Porn Star Gear will differ from that of being his Biker Chick... so decide how you're going to *Theme the Scene* when you choose your Porn Star Gear, and go from there. Get online and surf the website www.electriqueboutique.com for magnificent Porn Star costumes to *theme your scene.*

3.Get a Video/DVD Camcorder and a Tripod... if you're in a good relationship where you're sure that your man won't show his buddies (or worse) the Video/DVD... go ahead and tape your action, otherwise, you can just set-up the Video/DVD Camcorder on the tripod for 'effect'. Just use your personal discretion.

4. Get Porn Star Props... A) Home Depot has lovely oversized, full-length mirrors. You could set-one-up at the end of the bed or anywhere in your bedroom where your sexy booty is the main focus. B) Pole Dancing is another prop you can utilize, and you can buy a removable dancer's pole at www.poledanzer.com and then you can take lessons on how to Pole Dance if you purchase a DVD from www.polecatsdvd.com. Many towns and cities now have studios where Pole Dancing classes are taught. C) Giving your man access to a digital camera or Polaroid camera are other props that you can use. For more ideas, watch a few porn movies to get Porn Star props and porn star attitude-concepts!

5. Get Porn Star Comfy Afterward... after you've done him like a Porn Star, you can still show him that you're his sexy Porn Star by purchasing naughty sleep-wear from www.pornstarclothing.com. They have sexy bed wear that will put your pretty Porn Star pussy right to sleep.

Private Dancer Specialties:

How to... Become a *Sexy Mommy*

A good friend once told me that my usage of the words 'sexy and mommy' in sequence, was an oxy-moron. I don't see it that way, because none of us would have become mothers if we hadn't had sex! Most of my girlfriends are mothers and nearly all of the women who read this are mothers, and if you aren't a mother yet your day will ultimately come, so what is said here next also applies to all women.

I spent all of my twenties dodging any man who spoke about marriage and children because I was a sexy girl and I had better and brighter plans for my future. Then, while I was still blissfully single at the age of 30 (and with all credit going to a failed Depo-Provera shot!), I got pregnant and had a baby boy. Ten years later, my plans were still the same as they were when I was without child... I've simply had to make adjustments. Since I am a writer and am always available, I've become the drop-off girl for the children of many friends, and there is rarely a moment of peace and quiet in my home. If I had not learned early on in my son's life to create and produce in an atmosphere of screaming chaos, well, my literary career would have died a peaceful and quiet death long, long ago! It was the same with my sex life: it took me some time to modify, but I am still That sexy girl, and a really, really sexy mommy... and if you're a mommy, I guarantee that you are still That sexy girl... it's just possible that you have not paid any attention to that other part of you for a very long time.

Because something distorted happens to a large magnitude of women after they've had children. And that something is not what men do to women it is a daily choice that women make. It's not having children or being exhausted or the constant multi-tasking women do that turns a very sexy girl into a very sexually-disconnected woman it is a woman's perception of Her Self that changes who she is. No other woman on Earth needs sexy panties and naughty lingerie sweet smelling body lotions and massage oils or sinful chocolates and satin sheets, like a mommy. That part of a woman's life should be a divine retreat from the daily grind of refereeing the kids, carpooling in the snow, working nine hours and coming home to five loads of dirty laundry and not having the aspiration to make anything for dinner but Hamburger Helper.

When you just drop into bed without receiving or bestowing any romantic attention to your husband or lover, it eventually depletes who you are and it kills your romantic relationship with him. And the longer you ignore your needs and your man's needs, the easier it gets for you to convince yourself that it's acceptable to sacrifice your emotional and physical needs for the sake of being Super Mom, until you finally reach that point where lacy panties seem ridiculous and a chick flick is the only place you feel romance is the real deal.

You've raised your kids to do their chores correctly, and given a great deal of attention to their needs, and if you no longer see the sexy girl you once were, you need to re-think the way that you are still raising yourself. You are not just a mother; you are still a chick with unlimited potential and obtainable goals, and your needs are just as significant as those of your children. You cannot be a first-rate mommy if you have stopped being good to yourself... or to your man.

On a daily basis, my house is overrun with something CHILD: Lego blocks, noisy X-Box games, cereal left on the floor from a baby of a friend, Sponge Bob Square Pants videos, and "I'm telling! You gave me a dirty look!" or being ignored by my teenager.

My bedroom is my retreat.

And I refuse to surrender to the chaos.

I can balance, because I choose to. So can you. It only takes a few small steps to change your perspective of yourself.

Now is a good day to begin, and here are a few suggestions:

Start by incorporating your sex life in-spite your children's schedule, and *no longer around your children's schedule.* You can begin this with the **Closed-Door Policy**.

For example: perhaps you work an 11pm to 7am shift at the hospital five-nights-a-week and your husband works 9am to 6pm. Why should you have to wait five days to get any nookie? Your options are not limitless. Make dinner, give the kids a bath, get them a bedtime snack, put a ½ hour video in for them, and then close your bedroom door for that ½ hour. You'll have resistance from them: they'll bang on the door, they'll insist they need you, they'll make every excuse for you to open that door, but the longer you resist opening that door, the sooner they'll understand that when the door is closed to your bedroom, that means closed. When enforcing the **Closed-Door Policy**, set your mind to that place when you were potty-training your child or getting your child off the pacifier. Teach your child to respect that your **Closed-Door Policy** means uninterrupted personal time for adults.

Throw out your old panties and buy new ones with satin or lace or sexy suggestions or pretty metal hooks. And while you're at it, get some eye-catching lingerie. And don't give me the excuse that you cannot find any in your size. I have been 5'11 since the seventh grade and I could challenge Xena to a duel! Your size is not special, so get out and buy some sexy panties!

Purchase: a red or black pair of thigh-high stockings; a red lipstick; stick-on body jewels; body glitter; hair glitter; chandelier earrings; a fake pearl necklace.

Stock a Bedroom Box. Buy a large, pretty wooden box with a closed-hook at stores like Target, TJ Maxx or Ross. Stock it with sexy items such as Karma Sutra Love Oils, sweet-tasting sex lubricants, massage cream, and place it in a corner in your bedroom. If you need more ideas for what to stock in your Bedroom Box, then you should visit websites:
www.babeland.com
www.Xandria.com
www.Partygals.com

Or go to stores like Spencer's Gifts, Frederick's of, Hollywood, or Victoria's Secret.

Visit: the sex/relationship section at Barnes & Noble, or your local bookstore, and read-up on what's been written since you've been away. Or buy yourself a racy romance novel and be ready for your man the first chance you get!

How To... Give your man the Perfect Gift

Men are so weary of ties and cologne... it's a wonder that they don't complain about the repetitive gifts that they receive every Father's Day, Christmas and every birthday! I love shopping for a man... and nothing is more sensuous than a woman who *Knows* her man and what it takes to really search *The Globe* for that *One Gift* that will entice him... excite him... and blow his little boy mind!? www.findgift.com takes gift-giving for your man from the thoughtful-n-sweet to the brilliantly extreme... and it has sources where you can get your hands on *The Most* Magnificent gift for your man on the planet! What's so wonderful about giving your man 'the perfect gift' is that he will see just how much thought you put into it... and just how much he means to you. It has the *Perfect* gift for *Any Man*! Here are just a few fantastic ideas taken from the website www.findgift.com... and where you can find 'It' for your man.

A Real Share of Playboy Stock... Wow him with a true single share ownership that entitles the shareholder to declared dividends and annual reports. Framed with engraved personalized plaque and with Hef's printed signature. www.giveashare.com

 1 Acre of Land on the Moon... 1 acre of land on the Moon-100% legal and real! Moon property is a great gift, a potential prudent investment and an interesting conversation piece. Attractive gift! www.lunarLandOwner.com

 Buy Land on Mars... One acre of land on Mars-yes it's true, you can give him land on Mars! Makes a great and unique gift or for a potential and prudent investment. www.lunarFederation.com

Own An Acre Of The Pacific Ocean... Own a one-acre deed to a claim of Pacific Ocean floor. Originally claimed to preserve our fragile undersea environment and protect it from seabed strip mining, this land is yours to do with as you please. www.thingsYouNeverKnewExisted.com

Your Faces on Adam and Eve Artwork... Imagine your photo seamlessly transformed onto Adam and Eve by our professional artists! Also available in 27 other styles. Preview your artwork online. Free revisions. www.mydavinci.com

A Real Share of Budweiser Stock... This Bud is Really For Him-one real share of Anheuser Busch stock. Shareholder gets dividends & annual reports. Can be framed and personalized with plaque. He'll love this! www.giveashare.com

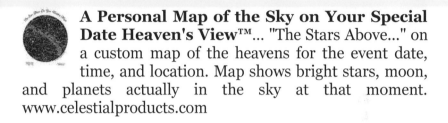 **A Personal Map of the Sky on Your Special Date Heaven's View**™... "The Stars Above..." on a custom map of the heavens for the event date, time, and location. Map shows bright stars, moon, and planets actually in the sky at that moment. www.celestialproducts.com

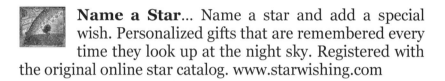 **Name a Star**... Name a star and add a special wish. Personalized gifts that are remembered every time they look up at the night sky. Registered with the original online star catalog. www.starwishing.com

 Monthly Ice Cream Club... Ice cream delivered each month for your man! Join for as many months as you want. www.icecreamsource.com

 Sailing Gift... Charter a sail boat, take a course or just sit back and enjoy the ride. We have something for everyone. Come get the wind! www.signaturedays.com

 New York City Helicopter Tour... Swoop past the Statue of Liberty, soar over Central Park, or experience the luxury of a private helicopter tour around the world's most celebrated skyline. www.xperiencedays.com

Hang Gliding Gift... Signature Days will help you dive from the sky in many ways and many locations. For a thrilling experience that He'll never forget you've come to the right place. www.signaturedays.com

 Ride or Drive a NASCAR Experience... Signature Days will satisfy his need for speed in many ways and many locations. For a thrilling experience that he'll never forget. www.signaturedays.com

 New York Schooner Sailing... Watch the Manhattan Skyline drift by as you sip Champagne onboard the Schooner Adirondack of an 80-foot wooden replica of a classic turn of the century pilot schooner. He'll love it! www.xperiencedays.com

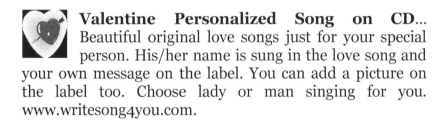 **Valentine Personalized Song on CD**... Beautiful original love songs just for your special person. His/her name is sung in the love song and your own message on the label. You can add a picture on the label too. Choose lady or man singing for you. www.writesong4you.com.

 Extreme Spa for Him... Spoil a man in your life with this ultimate spa basket--award-winning Baxter of California skincare items and plush terry robe and slippers will leave him relaxed, refreshed and ready for the next big adventure. www.travelbasketsinc.com

 **PARific Golf Gift Basket**... PARific is packed with Golfers delights! Featuring Ball Caddy Plus, Rules of Gold, Score Card, Golf Towel, Picture Frame and a Golf coffee or tea Mug. A golfer's delight!
www.designityourselfgiftbaskets.com

 Forever Ring Bookmark... Never lose your place again with this never fall out LITERATI Bookmark - a double-corded elasticized marker that snugly wraps around book spine and pages. Made with Lemon yellow, Jade, and Austrian crystals. www.menagerieroweintlinc.com

 Wristwatch Television... The digital display captures a crisp, clear 280 x 220 resolution picture on its 1 1/2" color monitor. Receives both UHF and VHF channels. www.hammacherschlemmer.com

 Personalized Romance Novels... Personalized romance novel set in the wild, wild west! An adventure of cowboys and cowgirls with passion and action, 160-page paperback novel with over 30 characteristics to personalize. Love, passion and humor in one gift! www.bookbyyoupublishing.com

 Rules of Golf Book... A better way to keep the foursome friendly with an official rulebook! Did you know that strokes made with the wrong ball don't count? www.redenvelope.com

How To... Make a Sexy Bedroom

Next time you watch a re-run of "Everybody Loves Raymond," take a good look at Ray and Deb's bedroom... and you'll realize that it is, without-a-doubt, the ugliest, most unromantic bedroom in sitcom history. No wonder their sex-life was written like a bore... I just don't see how a bedroom like that could inspire sleep, let alone romance or sex!

Oprah once did an entire hour on utterly unattractive and chaotic bedrooms and every time another revolting bedroom was shown, I inwardly winced. Who can become romantic in a bedroom with a television or computer, paper piles, tossed clothing, knick-knack clutter or uncomfortable and ghastly bed apparel? An unromantic bedroom kills sexual desire and any couple's longing to get closer emotionally. Your bedroom should be a place of serenity where you can re-charge your spirit, unwind, and feel sexy and romantic.

Miranda, from Sex and the City, saw the importance of having a sexy bedroom, and in one of their many Life-Learning conversations Miranda says to Carrie "I'm trying to change my bed karma. I figure if I can make my bed a place I really want to be, others will feel the same." And Carrie replies "Aah, the Field of Dreams." To which Miranda admits: "Exactly. If you build it, he will come."

You can easily change your bedroom within a few hours, or on any weekend that he's out doing guy stuff. Not only can you completely change the appearance and atmosphere of your bedroom with a few of these great ideas, but you can do it very inexpensively. Here's the idea list:

STEP ONE:

1. Get the computer or television out of the bedroom, as they are noisy distractions. If you feel that you must have a television in the bedroom, then move it to a wheelbase cart, and make room for it in a bedroom closet where you can easily remove it and replace it.

2. Keep the cells, pagers, iPods, and palm-pilots... all electronic devises, out of the bedroom and plugged-in elsewhere, overnight.

3. Take all unromantic clutter items... such as: a breast pump, paper piles, tweezers and toenail clippers, laundry baskets, tossed shoes, broken earrings, already-read books... and put all of these unromantic items in their proper places and away from any visual sight in your bedroom.

4. Clean off your dressers, and only leave these items to be placed back: candles, perfumes and pretty knick-knacks, photographs. Everything else goes someplace else. If you have nightstands, only leave one book and your glasses any of your needed items that don't over-clutter the eye.

5. Take a good look at your bedroom walls and decide if they need to be up-dated or re-painted. If you choose to do an update or a re-paint, then it will take an additional day to finish your bedroom as the paint will need to dry.

STEP TWO:

1. Decide what color motif you want. For instance, my color motif is dull gold and maroon. Once you've decided on your color scheme, it will be easy to search for what you need. One great idea is to go to www.bombaycompany.com and take a tour of all their lovely, romantic bedroom ideas. You can either buy from there or at one of their many stores or, you can...

2. Take off and go to Goodwill, Salvation Army, TJ Maxx, Marshall's, Ross or Burlington Coat Factory. You will find a wealth of lovely old or new romantic items, from furniture to candle sticks, in such materials as velvet, satin, crystal, old brass, wood. For instance: I found an old, comfy burnt-orange velvet chair for $5.00 at Goodwill, and I bought a maroon velvet throw for $9.00 at TJ Maxx and covered it over the chair, then added a small $5.00 maroon and gold pillow. Lovely and romantic!

3. Stock-up on really pretty room-theme picture frames, candlesticks and scented candles, comfy toss pillows, vases and lamps. Look for wall pictures and hangings of anything romantic. For instance: I found a large, beautiful mosaic picture of 'The Kiss' at TJ Maxx for $12.99, and a set of brass wall candle-holders for $4.00 at The Salvation Army.

4. Pick-up wooden or marble statues of couples in romantic poses, of pretty jewel boxes and bedroom-corner boxes. Make sure to get dresser-runners that fit the color-scheme of your bedroom. For instance: I found a set of romantic dancers, made in brass and then painted, at Burlington Coat Factory for $15.00 each, and I have a bedroom-corner box in every corner of my bedroom and dressers.

5. Find the exact bed-apparel set that fits your style... from deep purple satin bed comforter to intense red or bright yellow, in thick comforters in velvet or satin or soft cotton. Buy comfy cotton, satin, or silk sheets. Get the perfect matching curtains.

6. Change your entire bed, if you can afford it. Get that Canopy, Victorian, Sleigh bed, Four Poster... these types of beds just welcome romance and sex!

7. Get to Wal-Mart or Home Depot or Lowe's and buy the paint you've visualized for you bedroom if you're going to paint it, and make sure you've got plenty of nails and proper fixer-up equipment.

STEP THREE:

1. It will be easy to put it all together... you don't need a decorator's eye to make a great romantic bedroom... you're a chick and romance is in your basic instinct. After you've made-up the bed, put the runners on your dressers and added all your pretty new candles and picture frames and lovely statues and boxes and placed the curtains... you will immediately begin to feel *sexy, sexy, sexy.*

2. After you've gotten your bedroom all ready for peace, tranquility and gettin' downright good lovin,' now it's time to buy some new panties or pretty bedclothes and lingerie.

You should also get a bedroom box, where you can keep all your private romantic and sexual items on-hand for easy access. A bedroom-box has items such as: a mellow CD with exclusive songs you've downloaded off the internet just for sex; breath mints for Before and After; two chilled mini bottled waters; a mini flashlight (so you won't break the mood by switching on the light when searching in your Bedroom Box for all those naughty goodies); unscented baby wipes; lubricant and toys for sex.

3. For extra-ideas on what to have handy in your romantic bedroom: a small refrigerator stocked with wine, beer, bottled water and/or a shelf stocked with imperishable after-sex goodies; a high-shelf or locked-box with porn.

When my girlfriends come to my house, they love to hang-out and chat in my bedroom. It is the most peaceful, sexy and romantic place in my home. That's why I always have such wonderful and creative ideas!

Change your bedroom: change your Romantic life.

One step forward to All-Things Better.

How To... Tell him I Love You

Tell him **I Love You** in 100 different languages:

English - I love you
Afrikaans - Ek het jou life
Albanian - Te dua
Arabic - Ana behibak (to male)
Arabic - Ana behibek (to female)
Armenian - Yes kez sirumen
Bambara - M'bi fe
Bangla - Aamee tuma ke bhalo aashi
Belarusian - Ya tabe kahayu
Bisaya - Nahigugma ako kanimo
Bulgarian - Obicham te
Cambodian - Soro lahn nhee ah
Cantonese Chinese - Ngo oiy ney a
Catalan - T'estimo
Cheyenne - Ne mohotatse

Chichewa – Ndimakukonda
Corsican - Ti tengu caru (to male)
Creol - Mi aime jou
Croatian - Volim te
Czech - Miluji te
Danish - Jeg Elsker Dig
Dutch - Ik hou van jou
Esperanto - Mi amas vin
Estonian - Ma armastan sind
Ethiopian - Afgreki'
Faroese - Eg elski teg
Farsi - Doset daram
Filipino - Mahal kita
Finnish - Mina rakastan sinua
French - Je t'aime, Je t'adore
Gaelic - Ta gra agam ort
Georgian – Mikvarhar
German - Ich liebe dich
Greek - S'agapo
Gujarati - Hoo thunay prem karoo choo
Hiligaynon - Palangga ko ikaw
Hawaiian - Aloha wau ia oi
Hebrew - Ani ohev otah (to female)
Hebrew - Ani ohev et otha (to male)
Hiligaynon - Guina higugma ko ikaw
Hindi - Hum Tumhe Pyar Karte hae
Hmong - Kuv hlub koj
Hopi - Nu' umi unangwa'ta
Hungarian – Szeretlek
Icelandic - Eg elska tig
Ilonggo - Palangga ko ikaw
Indonesian - Saya cinta padamu
Inuit – Negligevapse
Irish - Taim i' ngra leat
Italian - Ti amo
Japanese – Aishiteru
Kannada - Naanu ninna preetisuttene
Kapampangan - Kaluguran daka
Kiswahili – Nakupenda

Konkani - Tu magel moga cho
Korean - Sarang Heyo
Latin - Te amo
Latvian - Es tevi miilu
Lebanese – Bahibak
Lithuanian - Tave myliu
Malay - Saya cintakan mu / Aku cinta padamu
Malayalam - Njan Ninne Premikunnu
Mandarin Chinese - Wo ai ni
Marathi - Me tula prem karto
Mohawk – Kanbhik
Moroccan - Ana moajaba bik
Nahuatl - Ni mits neki
Navaho - Ayor anosh'ni
Norwegian - Jeg Elsker Deg
Pandacan - Syota na kita!!

Pangasinan - Inaru Taka
Papiamento - Mi ta stimabo
Persian - Doo-set daaram
Pig Latin - Iay ovlay ouyay
Polish - Kocham Ciebie
Portuguese - Eu te amo
Romanian - Te iubesc
Russian - Ya tebya liubliu
Scot Gaelic - Tha gra'dh agam ort
Serbian - Volim te
Setswana - Ke a go rata
Sign Language - ,\„/ (represents position of fingers when signing'I Love You')
Sindhi - Maa tokhe pyar kendo ahyan
Sioux – Techihhila
Slovak - Lu`bim ta
Slovenian - Ljubim te
Spanish - Te quiero / Te amo
Swahili - Ninapenda wewe
Swedish - Jag alskar dig
Swiss-German - Ich lieb Di
Tagalog - Mahal kita
Taiwanese - Wa ga ei li

Tahitian - Ua Here Vau Ia Oe
Tamil - Nan unnai kathalikaraen
Telugu - Nenu ninnu premistunnanu
Thai - Chan rak khun (to male)
Thai - Phom rak khun (to female)
Turkish - Seni Seviyorum
Ukrainian - Ya tebe kahayu
Urdu - mai aap say pyaar karta hoo
Vietnamese - Anh ye^u em (to female)
Vietnamese - Em ye^u anh (to male)
Welsh - 'Rwy'n dy garu
Yiddish - Ikh hob dikh
Yoruba - Mo ni fe

How To... Word Magic Your Man

I will gladly admit that until I read books written by author Tracy Cabot, Ph.D, that I was unaware that, according to Tracy *"... having the same communication style or using the communication style that your partner is using greatly avoids missed connections, unnecessary challenges and increase intimacy by reducing the events of resentment. Passion starts to fade away when there is build up resentments. Communicating the right way is one of the tools to keep lasting romance. There are 3 types of Love Language: you have the* **Visual***, the* **Auditory** *and the* **Feeling** *style. We use all of those 3 ways to communication but one is predominant."*

Tracy further explains this in her book *How to Make a Man Fall in Love with You,* and I will never, ever say it better than Tracy can... so here it is in her own words:

Visual expresses enthusiasm or stress similar to those comments: "Don't you **see** *how this is amazing?!" or " You'll* **see***. You'll love it" or " You don't* **look** *in a great shape today". An Auditory will say "This* **sounds** *good" when a Feeling will say "This* **feels** *good. I have the* **impression** *that will work" or "I know how you* **feel***" or "I understand."*

With **Visual**, it's the look that counts. They usually are well dressed. They take care of their appearance. They relax in a beautiful, well harmonized environment. Things have to be in order around them. They look for partners who take care of their looks too. When visual think, their eyes look up in the air because they are "visualizing" what they will say or the situation in their mind. They will tell you "how things looked". They don't talk about their feelings early in the relationship because they need to "see" where the relationship is leading first. They like to watch television, read, arts, landscaping, etc., anything that stimulates their eyes.

Auditory are very sensitive the sounds around them. They always have music at home or in their car. They talk a lot because they like to "hear" themselves talk. They are easily distracted by noise. They adore being talked softly in the ear. The quality of the voice of their partner can be a true turn on or a definitive turn off. An Auditory will look on the side when they think because they have to hear the voice in their head. Auditory will tell you "how things sounds." Auditory will have the latest stereo system in town, they prefer going to concerts, they like to talk on the phone and they have a special talent for music.

Feeling reacts on intuitions and their guts. They are willing to sacrifice elegance for comfort (no high heels for women and tight collar shirt for men). They want to feel great at all times and in every situation. They look for partners who are great at sharing feelings. They are perceived as people with a great heart. Women are easily seduced by Feeling Men because they have the ability to express their sensitive side and are great listeners, so common to women's needs. Feeling people like to touch, to kiss and they greatly need a constant physical expression from their partner. Feeling people look down when they think because they need to get the "impression". Feeling people will tell you "how things felt". They like to relax lye in the sun, work out, massage, drink, and dance, and eat great foods. They will most likely do risky activities *because of the rush of extreme sensations. They are looking for trills.*

If you are with a partner that has the same communication style as yours, enjoy yourselves. If you have two different communication styles, don't conclude that you are not made for one another and it's maybe time to see a counselor (a therapist or a lawyer!). This article will give you more tools to help communication at the maximum and get a deeper connection with your mate or future mate.

How can we capture the heart of a Visual, an Auditory or a Feeling person?

*With **Visuals**, you need to use visual terms; from my "perspective", I can "see" what you mean, the more I "look" into this, the more it "seems" nice, I "observed" how wonderful you are with kids, etc.. Visual need to be stimulated with what they see; always have a neat house, with harmonized colors, be dressed elegantly in every situation (wearing jeans can be elegant with a nice matching color and style top). Be sexy. For lovemaking, always have a little light, or candle, because it turns them on to see their partner enjoying sex. Look in the eyes show them that you care for them and you are attentive. Visuals like to make scenarios. They usually don't rush in the lovemaking because they need to admire first. They need to "see" it. Also, they don't communicate in words their feelings. They show them instead. Be sensitive to their generosity. Don't share your feelings too early in the relationship. Show them instead how you feel and how you are. They'll get the picture.*

***Auditory** will be worried about the noise in the house. Quietness and great music atmosphere sure gets them to come around often. Use a soft voice when speaking to them even when you are fighting. You will need to speak in sound language; your voice "turns" me on, that has a negative "ring", "tell me, what do you think? I'm "listening", this sounds "wonderful", the "rhythm" is* *perfect, etc.. Think verbal reassurance. Looking in the eye won't have the same effect. Auditory often ask if you love them. For lovemaking, use a sensual sweet "radio voice" in their ear. Describe how you feel during the heat of the passion. Sounds of lovemaking will have a powerful effect on them. They usually don't notice the new dress or new haircut that you just had, but they will gladly listen on how you got that new dress or new haircut, as long as they are in an environment that allows listening. They are really interested in who you are. Not on how you look. They are the best listeners.*

*With a **Feeling** person, use feelings word; that "feels" good, I'd hate to "disappoint you", I don't really "connect" with that person, I can't wait to "touch" you, I "feel" that we are going somewhere, let me give you a "massage", etc... they can be perceived a passionate people because they express their feelings so much. They need to know how you feel, very early in the relationship.*

They expect to be touched by their partner a lot and they do the same. They often complain about insensitivity of their partners. Play with their hair while you talk to them, in the car, while you are driving, keep one hand on the leg, take walks and hold hands, wear satin underwear, make hot bath, etc... feeling people can make lovemaking in any situation because they need the touch only. They are not necessarily the neat one or the most elegant either, but they will truly appreciate the complete you.

*Pay attention of the dominant type of you and your partner's. **Practice** the appropriate communication style until it becomes natural. Reducing challenges in a relationship increases the chances of lasting romance. Now, you have a way to capture the heart of anyone that you want, if you are single, and you can re-ignite the fire if you are in an unsatisfying relationship and get what you and your partner wants, because the connection will be deeper. I am a strong believer of "say anything that you want" to your partner. But, there are ways of saying things. You just learned on how to make yourself heard* *and understood properly and receive your partner's needs and caring expressions right.*

No relationship expert has ever said it any better than Tracy Cabot. I know, I've searched and searched the Internet, and no one proves how you can Word Magic your man better than Tracy! For more on Tracy and all her book, please go to www.tracycabot.com.

Funny business, a woman's career; the things you drop on your way up the ladder so you can move faster; you'll forget you'll need them again when you get back to being a woman. Nothing's any good unless you can look-up just before dinner or turn around in bed and there he is. Without that, you're not a woman; you're something with a French provincial office or a book full of clippings. But you're not a woman.

~~~Bette Davis in *All About Eve*

Private Dancer Excellent Reads

If you really want to become the best lover he's ever had, not in just word or wish but in theory... than read... because there is no better research available for your Goddess-gleaning. The ideas, opinions, concepts, history and facts that you will learn from books, guarantee that whatever knowledge you gain from your mental travels, will be more-than enough to entice him until he's a wrinkled old man in a retirement home. Some context of book description narrated by www.amazon.com.

 The Japanese Art Of Sex How to Tease, Seduce, And Pleasure the Samurai in Your Bedroom, by Jina Bacarr, is the best book I have ever read on how to treat him like a Daimyo.

Zen Sex, by Phillip Toshio Sudo... shows that anyone who desires more fulfilling sex can put the classic Zen principles offered here into practice in their lives. Zen parables, koans, and poems illuminate Sudo's message, meditations encourage pause and reflection, and exercises get you started on the Way of Making Love, Zen style. Great sex, zen sex, reminds us that we are ever alive and full of love. In making love, our bodies intertwined, we are at one with ourselves, each other, and with the very source of life. Every night of passion becomes an opportunity to elevate the human spirit.

 Sex and Spirit: an Illustrated Guide to Techniques and Traditions, by John Gray and John Selby... shows you how to bring sex to the level of spirituality and inner-grace.

 Making Sex, by Thomas Laqueur... This is a book about the making an unmaking of sex over the centuries. It tells the astonishing story of sex in West from the ancients to the moderns in a precise account of the history of reproductive anatomy and physiology.

 Encyclopedia of Unusual Sex Practices by Brenda Love... Trust me when I tell you that this book will prove just how kinky, kinky really is!

 Sex Magick, by Donald Micheal Kraig... This is one of the first books to clearly reveal the secrets of Western sex magick without relying on Tantric theory. It explores the latest scientific discoveries in the field of human sexuality. 55 line illustrations.

Sex in History, by Reay Tannahill... was such an interesting read that I added it to my home library. You will find so much information in this book about what men... and women!.. have done for the lust of the flesh!

 Sex and the Perfect Lover, by Mabel Iam... Tao, Tantra, and the Kama Sutra... takes your sex with him to that Other Level. You will truly be glad that you read this book.

 Sex with Kings... 500 Years of Adultery, Power, Rivalry, and Revenge, by Eleanor Herman... Throughout the centuries, royal mistresses have been worshiped, feared, envied, and reviled. They set the fashions, encouraged the arts, and, in some cases, ruled nations. Eleanor Herman's Sex with Kings takes us into the throne rooms and bedrooms of Europe's most powerful monarchs. Alive with flamboyant characters, outrageous humor, and stirring poignancy, this glittering tale of passion and politics chronicles five hundred years of scintillating women and the kings who loved them.

 Sex and the Paranormal, by Paul Deane... Peer for the first time into dark corners where basic human physical desire meets with the unknown, mysterious, and supernatural. From ghost rape to demon lovers, here are the most startling manifestations of paranormal sexuality. Written by a scientist and leading member of the highly respected British organization Society for Psychical Research, this study is revelatory, thought provoking, and most certainly sensational. It presents thousands of reports of human sexual encounters with otherworldly beings that have occurred over the years. (Just two of the startling chapters are Satanism in the Suburbs and Aliens Stole My Virginity.)

These meetings appear entirely common, with people claiming relationships with poltergeists and angels. Then, too, there are the strange examples of outbreaks of sexual mass hysteria and a firm belief in supernatural orgies. The wealth of stories is nothing short of amazing, the phenomena almost beyond belief, and the author's unique talent for providing both entertainment and a serious account unequalled.

 Sex, by Anne Hooper... Every woman should have a bedside library including... Great Sex Games to put the sizzle back into sex with daring and erotic games, Kama Sutra to discover ancient sexual wisdom for modern lovers, and Great Sex Guide for a stimulating mind and body program to unleash your sexual energy. Mini manuals for mega enjoyment!

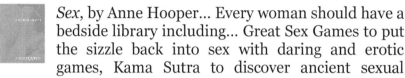 *The French Maid*, by Debra and Don McLeod... In the bookshops, on the Internet, and in the toy stores, women are flocking to the new female-empowered world of sex books and products more than ever before. The feminine touch is changing the way naughty treats are crafted, making for a woman-driven and powerfully arousing brand of eroticism. And the authors of Sex Scenes have their fingers on the pulse of this risqué revolution.

A married couple, Debra and Don Macleod were tired of the tame, predictable advice offered by typical spice-up-your-love-life sex guides. So they hit the sheets to produce this deliciously playful guide to help women turn up the heat using the seductive power of erotic fantasy.

Filled with 22 step-by-step fully-scripted love scenes, this fun (and filthy) handbook shows women how to be their sexiest selves by opening up the world of sexual fantasy to their men. Want to play doctor? Sex Scenes relies on sexy storytelling and hot and heavy sexual action, with each explicit fantasy providing plot, dialogue, and complete directions for consummating the wickedest bedroom scenes ever. Inside, you'll find classics like the Naughty Babysitter and the Massage That Is More Than a Massage, to newly imagined romps like Adult House Party and the Camping Trip. With Sex Scenes doing all the work, readers can have the confidence to surprise and arouse their men with their wildest fantasies come true!

 Sex Secrets of Escorts by Veronica Monet... shows you that what men desire, want and need is exactly how I've put it to you in this book!

 Tricks and Treats: Sex Workers Write about Their Clients, edited by Matt Bernstein Sycamore... read how other people's sex lives are always interesting-we all love to hear the dirt-but the sex lives of professional escorts are more interesting than most. Tricks and Treats is full of wonderful, often hilarious, sometimes touching stories."

 How to be a Sex Goddess by Sarah Tomszak... Everything you need to know to let your inner sex goddess shine through. This is a great manual for spicing up your love life.

 The Goddess in the Bedroom, by Z Budapest... A women's guide to sexuality presents erotic ideas, recipes, positions, decorating tips, cleansing rituals, and energy-focusing techniques. Written by the author of The Goddess in the Office.

The Complete Idiot's Guide to Being a Sex Goddess, by Stacy Clark and Eve Adamson... the easy way! Just grab this book and do a quick flip-n-find to get a great Goddess idea!

 Seduction: Tempt, Tease and Tantalize your Lover, by Snow Raven Starborn... is such a beautiful book, I highly recommend it to every woman who wants to love her man from his heart, to his body, to his mind. Filled with poetry, lovely seductive meals and sensual ideas to turn his heart around, this book is a must-have!

 Phone Sex, by Miranda Austin... gives you all kinds of wonderful ideas to turn your man on whenever he is away... or just driving home! For singles and couples who want to add safe, thrilling phone sex to their sexual repertoire. A professional phone sex worker shares her secrets of aural sex, and plenty of juicy anecdotes culled from thousands of weird and wonderful sex calls. For the sexually adventurous, distance is no longer an obstacle.

 Down and Dirty Sex Secrets: the New and Naughty Guide to Being Great in Bed, by Tristan Taormino... A veritable buffet of human sexuality... no matter how good you think your sex life is, this book is bound to give you a few ideas on how to make it even better. Tristan Taormino has garnered popular and critical raves for talking unabashedly about every sexual taboo. In *Down and Dirty Sex Secrets*, she uses her singular voice to redefine the sex primer. Tristan breathes new life into the classics— oral sex, multiple orgasms, and hitting that elusive G-spot, just to name a few— with humor, intelligence, and firsthand expertise. But she also introduces a new set of sexual fundamentals—strap-ons, female ejaculation, erotica, S&M, sex toys, and more— for all those looking to expand their sexual repertoire and improve their sex life dramatically. Quite simply, this is an indispensable guide to mind-blowing, twenty-first-century sex.

 Love Potions and Charms: Over 50 Ways to Seduce, Bewitch, and Cherish Your Lover, by Francis Melville... If love really makes the world go 'round, here's a book that will heighten the spin. It's all about enticing a lover, with more than 50 recipes for perfumes, love charms, aphrodisiacs, and lovers' magic spells. Author and herbal expert Francis Melville explains how to attract and hold a lover by using herbs, as well as commonly available foods, flowers, spices, and other ingredients. Everything discussed in these pages is as pure and as natural as sex appeal itself. For instance, few aphrodisiacs are more wholesome, or more effective, than well prepared fish entrees, oysters on the half-shell—or for very special occasions, caviar. This beautifully illustrated book's highlights include: recipes for the foods of love; directions for making flower garlands and other delightful accessories to enhance the scene of love; rituals passed down through the generations to attract a lover, including instructions for using the world's most alluring scents; ways to make magic charms that will entice a chosen lover... and more. Beautiful full-color illustrations abound throughout this book, making it a delight to the eye as well as the imagination. Here are ideas, advice, and directions meant for everyone who will ever fall in love.

 Over 100 Triple X Sex Tricks, by Lisa Sussman... this book gives you and 'in' to how the porn stars Do It!

Kissing School, by Cherie Byrd... Enduring a terrible kiss can be more than just unpleasant. It can add tension to intimate moments, or worse, end a great romance before it even starts. After personally saving a relationship by teaching her partner how to kiss, Cherie Byrd transformed the experience into her successful Kissing School! program, in which hundreds of couples from around the world have since participated. Kissing School distills the workshop's most useful teachings, and quickly ushers readers beyond quick pecks and "Can you feel my tongue?" action to enter a realm of soul-stirring, heart-lifting, body-shaking kissing. Seven in-depth lessons cover every aspect of technique and style without neglecting the spiritual and emotional aspects of the kissing experience. Homework assignments and other lively sidebars are included, as well as thoughtful pearls of wisdom from Byrd's Tantric and Taoist studies.

 Sex Disasters: And How to Survive Them, by Charles Moser, Janet W. Hardy and Charles Moser, MD... is a humorous, helpful look at the scary side of sex: • "Well, she said she was eighteen." • "Hey, where'd the condom go?" • "Eww, how do I get these stains out of the sheets?" Top sex educators and a consulting team of attorneys, cops, EMTs, therapists and sex educators team up to create an enjoyable--and factually accurate--guide to surviving awkward moments in the bedroom, back seat, or bushes. Learn what to do about • a jammed handcuff • a short-circuited vibrator • a cop peering in your car window.

 How to have Sex in the Woods, by Luann Colombo... Romantically inclined lovers... of the great outdoors will appreciate this guide to preparing for sex on a camping trip, which addresses such vital topics as how to pack and protect condoms, how to avoid skin contact with dangerous plants, and how to properly cushion a sleeping space.

1001 Sex Secrets Every Woman Should Know, by Chris Allen... gives away all the secrets of prostitutes and madams.

 Intercourses: An Aphrodisiac Cookbook, by Martha Hopkins and Randall Lockridge... are a delicious blending of beautiful photography and aphrodisiac recipes that even the novice cook can follow. The book is more than just a collection of recipes and pretty photos, it also includes information on massage, erogenous zones, astrology and other tips to improve your love life and your dinner. It's a treat for your recipient and anyone lucky enough to share in their new culinary skills.

 Brain Sex: The Real Difference Between Men and Women, by Anne Moir and David Jessel... proves, without doubt, just how differently his brain is from yours. I cannot stress this enough: **Get this book and study it like a bible. No one talks men and the way they think like this book!**

 *Sexual Function in People with Disability and Chronic Illness* by Marca L. Sipski and Craig J. Alexander... shows you how to be sexually active, despite disability and illness. Everyone wants to be touched... especially those who are ill. ? This book is beautifully written.

Spiritual Sex and Sex Secrets, by Michelle Pauli... offers practical tips as well as creative inspiration, these books provide guidance in all aspects of the sexual experience in straightforward, tasteful language. With insight for setting the mood and seducing partners, each volume covers a different approach to lovemaking, from the sacred and spiritual to the playful and provocative. Each offers useful advice for enriching and enlivening loving relationships: ancient sacred techniques for spiritual fulfillment; methods revealed in erotic Eastern texts; spicy scenarios for realizing fantasies; and tantalizing secrets for fun, lively sex. Inspiring extracts from a range of sources such as the Kama Sutra, Japanese pillow books, and Arab proverbs are featured throughout the text, along with quotations from writers and philosophers such as Walt Whitman, Anaïs Nin, and Charles Baudelaire.

I would like to acknowledge all the Sex Experts and Sex Goddesses I have featured in this chapter. Thank you for your immeasurable contribution to bettering-of sex, love and romantic relationships.

aphrodisiacsbondagecumdisciplineextrasfetishesgodhandmagicaphrodi
siacsbondagecumdisciplineextrasfetishesgodhandmagicaphrodisiacsbo
ndagecumdisciplineextrasfetishesgodhandmagicaphrodisiacsbondagecu
mdisciplineextrasfetishesgodhandmagicaphrodisiacsbondagecumdiscip
lineextrasfetishesgodhandmagicaphrodisiacsbondagecumdisciplineext
rasfetishesgodhandmagicaphrodisiacsbondagecumdisciplineextrasfeti
shesgodhandmagicaphrodisiacsbondagecumdisciplineextrasfetishesgod
handmagicaphrodisiacsbondagecumdisciplineextrasfetishesgodhandmag
icaphrodisiacsbondagecumdisciplineextrasfetishesgodhandmagicaphro
disiacsbondagecumdisciplineextrasfetishesgodhandmagicaphrodisiacs
bondagecumdisciplineextrasfetishesgodhandmagicaphrodisiacsbondage

The ABC's of Fucking

cumdisciplineextrasfetishesgodhandmagicaphrodisiacsbondagecumdisc
iplineextrasfetishesgodhandmagicaphrodisiacsbondagecumdisciplinee
xtrasfetishesgodhandmagicaphrodisiacsbondagecumdisciplineextrasfe
tishesgodhandmagicaphrodisiacsbondagecumdisciplineextrasfetishesg
odhandmagicaphrodisiacsbondagecumdisciplineextrasfetishesgodhandm
agicaphrodisiacsbondagecumdisciplineextrasfetishesgodhandmagicaph
rodisiacsbondagecumdisciplineextrasfetishesgodhandmagicaphrodisia
csbondagecumdisciplineextrasfetishesgodhandmagicaphrodisiacsbonda
gecumdisciplineextrasfetishesgodhandmagicaphrodisiacsbondagecumdi
sciplineextrasfetishesgodhandmagicaphrodisiacsbondagecumdisciplin
eextrasfetishesgodhandmagicaphrodisiacsbondagecumdisciplineextras
fetishesgodhandmagicaphrodisiacsbondagecumdisciplineextrasfetishe
sgodhandmagicaphrodisiacsbondagecumdisciplineextrasfetishesgodhan
dmagicaphrodisiacsbondagecumdisciplineextrasfetishesgodhandmagica
phrodisiacsbondagecumdisciplineextrasfetishesgodhandmagicaphrodis
iacsbondagecumdisciplineextrasfetishesgodhandmagicaphrodisiacsbon
dagecumdisciplineextrasfetishesgodhandmagicaphrodisiacsbondagecum
disciplineextrasfetishesgodhandmagicaphrodisiacsbondagecumdiscipl
ineextrasfetishesgodhandmagicaphrodisiacsbondagecumdisciplineextr
asfetishesgodhandmagicaphrodisiacsbondagecumdisciplineextrasfetis
hesgodhandmagicaphrodisiacsbondagecumdisciplineextrasfetishesgodh
andmagicaphrodisiacsbondagecumdisciplineextrasfetishesgodhandmagi
caphrodisiacsbondagecumdisciplineextrasfetishesgodhandmagicaphrod
isiacsbondagecumdisciplineextrasfetishesgodhandmagicaphrodisiacsb
ondagecumdisciplineextrasfetishesgodhandmagicaphrodisiacsbondagec
umdisciplineextrasfetishesgodhandmagicaphrodisiacsbondagecumdisci
plineextrasfetishesgodhandmagicaphrodisiacsbondagecumdisciplineex
trasfetishesgodhandmagicaphrodisiacsbondagecumdisciplineextrasfet
ishesgodhandmagicaphrodisiacsbondagecumdisciplineextrasfetishesgo
dhandmagicaphrodisiacsbondagecumdisciplineextrasfetishesgodhandma
gicaphrodisiacsbondagecumdisciplineextrasfetishesgodhandmagicaphr
odisiacsbondagecumdisciplineextrasfetishesgodhandmagicaphrodisiac
sbondagecumdisciplineextrasfetishesgodhandmagicaphrodisiacsbondag
ecumdisciplineextrasfetishesgodhandmagicaphrodisiacsbondagecumdis
ciplineextrasfetishesgodhandmagicaphrodisiacsbondagecumdiscipline
extrasfetishesgodhandmagicaphrodisiacsbondagecumdisciplineextrasf
etishesgodhandmagicaphrodisiacsbondagecumdisciplineextrasfetishes
godhandmagicaphrodisiacsbondagecumdisciplineextrasfetishesgodhand
magicaphrodisiacsbondagecumdisciplineextrasfetishesgodhandmagicap
hrodisiacsbondagecumdisciplineextrasfetishesgodhandmagicaphrodisi
acsbondagecumdisciplineextrasfetishesgodhandmagicaphrodisiacsbond
agecumdisciplineextrasfetishesgodhandmagicaphrodisiacsbondagecumd
isciplineextrasfetishesgodhandmagicaphrodisiacsbondagecumdiscipli
neextrasfetishesgodhandmagicaphrodisiacsbondagecumdisciplineextra

XV. The ABC's of Fucking
In America, sex is an obsession;
in other parts of the world, it is a Fact.

~~~Marlene Dietrich

Artwork featured at www.gradiva.com

Aphrodisiacs: kiss him with the herb Cardamom under your tongue, it is sworn to make him wiltingly yours. Chocolate, Oysters and liqueur are yummy Aphrodisiacs that romantically service your lover. Of course, the only true Aphrodisiac is your mind and how hot you know you are. Use your mind skillfully and your imagination pleasingly, and you can and will, get any man into your bed. For more information on the potent influence of Aphrodisiacs, purchase the books '*Love Elixirs*' and '*Love Potions*', or visit the New York store, *Enchantments*. If you just can't visit the store, go online to www.enchantmentsny.com for their sexually enchanting online catalogue full of aphrodisiac tips!

Bondage: *Helpless Sex* - which is your being tied-up during sex or you tying-up your lover during sex - is the most popular of sex games in numerous bedrooms round the Planet. For good planning, safety techniques and additional information about bondage, please go online and visit these websites: www.sportsheets.com & www.bedroombondage.com.

Cum: that whitish, yellowish creamy stuff that shoots out of his cock at orgasm and dribbles out a little before. Cum is the least fattening fluid you'll ever swallow... although it has the consistency of snot and can sometimes be an acquired taste, depending on how healthy your man is! Men idolize their cum and are completely obsessed with the whole 'idea' of it. It will greatly improve your sexual relationship with him if you become just-as, or even-more obsessed with his cum than he is. Tell him to spurt his cum in your face, on your breasts, into the crack of your ass, into your hair, on the curve of your back or into your bellybutton. He'll be thrilled.

Discipline: many men get-off on this type of sex - being 'forced' to adhere to the demands of a Mistress - which can be any action from begging and obedience to licking a woman's shoes or suffering humiliation with a paddle. For more information about Discipline, please go online and Search Engine the phrase Sexual Discipline, or take time and visit these websites: www.stormyleather.com and www.adulttoychest.com

Extras: these are absolute essentials for any woman who is a great fuck. You should have numerous sex toys, special lotions and oils, pleasurable couple games, massage oil and creams, and seductive lingerie in your lusty repertoire. Extras will make your sex healthier, and keep the life, fun and passion in your romantic relationship.

Fetishes: Swinging, Bondage, Cross-Dressing, S&M, Doms & Subs, Feet and Shoes, Spanking or Whipping, Watersports, Frottage, Infantilism, Amputeeism... you think it can't be out there, trust me, it is out there! For more information than I could ever give you on sexual fetishes, please go online and *AskJeeves* Search, *Google* Search or *Yahoo!* Search, the phrase Sex Fetishes.

God: there has been a nasty rumor since the Puritan Age, that sex is an abomination to 'God.' Get real. If you imagine, know, think, trust, believe, hope or even consider that there is a God and that He is/could be the inventor of sex, then how the fuck could you rationalize that sex is an abomination to Him? Fucking is, to your human body and to your emotional well-being, a biological need equivalent to water, food, and sleep. If you aren't fucking your man enough, then that is definitely why you are so emotionally miserable and so often feel so immeasurably lonely; and that isn't God's fault, it's yours!

Hand Magic: any woman who understands a man's body and knows how to expertly move her hands all over it, all in it, and all about it... this will warp a man's psyche into a state of vegetation. Promise!

Imagination: the *one and only* asset that any woman needs to keep her man. Take and use your naughty, delicious, delightful imagination to the Sexual Outer Limits and render him into your worshiping slave.

Jagging-off: watching a man stroke his cock is so exhilarating it'll illustrate why men are so visual and it'll clue-you-in to learning his hand-rhythm when he masturbates alone. Mutual Masturbation is also a plus because it's a real turn-on for him when you touch yourself, and you can teach him how to pop! your come-button as skillfully as you do.

Kisses: a great amount of kissing is a Must before, during and after any sexual interlude. The intensity of making-out and of giving him hot, wet, passionate kisses, is the best way to ease him into the end of the day... wake him up from sleep... or change his stubborn mind - and you can take him exactly where you want him. For brilliant ideas on all sorts of lovely ways to brandish him with your kisses, purchase the book titled '*The Art of Kissing.*'

Lusty Love Notes: nothing is sexier or sweeter than a lusty love note that narrates to him exactly what you intended to do to him, with him or for him... and what you're feeling about him, dreaming in regard to him, or hoping for with him. Write it, text it, email it, send it snail-mail - just pen it all out for him - because no man can resist a woman who really wants him. Put your lust in print, it will last forever.

Mindscrew: sexing-up his mind is always the best place to start foreplay. Talk to his mind with your eyes, your body, your ideas and your imagination. You must twist-tie his mind so tightly that he cannot concentrate on *anything* but the thought of being between your wet thighs.

Naughtywear: an absolute essential for any woman in any sexual interlude, who wants to be a Sex Goddess. Men love stockings, crotch-less panties, and fuck-me pumps. Yes, it really is that simple.

Orals: I cannot stress this enough - be user-friendly with your man's cock... mouth-music it to the max. And educate him to love, lick, slurp your pussy. *Orality is the red-hot key to sexual morality in your romantic relationship.*

Positions: much to my dismay, too many sex experts are obsessed with explaining sexual positions in text-book, pictorial detail. I trust that you are a smart girl and that you know what sort of twists, turns and flexibility your body is capable of doing - so, the last thing you need is more explanation on positions! Besides, the only true position book is the '*Kama Sutra*' and anything else you read is just a knock off. So purchase a '*Kama Sutra*' book if you think you need more information on positions. I recommend any '*Kama Sutra*' book written book by brilliant Sexologist Anne Hooper.

Quickies: this kind of sex is good and is much fun, and can be done anytime, anyplace and anywhere.

Rear Erotics: his ass, as well as yours - is a fundamental erogenous zone and a cryptic sexual cache that he will never forget that *you* discovered for him. *Around-the-world* the pucker of his ass-hole just once... and you'll be The Goddess. Promise!

Sex Exercises: you can tighten-up your vaginal muscles by these simple exercises:

1) *Quick-Stop*: clench your vaginal muscles in and then stop mid-piss when you're going to the bathroom. Keep practicing this move until you can hold your pee back five minutes, with your clenched vaginal muscles.

2) *Closet Clench*: anytime, anywhere, anyplace... tense your vaginal muscles by a quick clenching and tightening in-and-out movement. No one will know you're doing it, which is exactly why you have no excuse for not starting right now.

3) *Pussy Pops*: push your vaginal muscles in & out hard and steadily, twenty times, as if you were having a bowel movement.

4) *Pelvis-Roll Thrust*: lie on the floor with your back level, your arms straight against your sides, and your hips in the air; knees bent and feet flat. Thrust forward with your hips, and then roll your lower body side-to-side like a swing. Repeat twenty times.

5) *Super Kegal Exercisers*: The Original: shaped like an inner thigh master, this pussy exerciser tones and strengthens the vaginal muscles as well as your lower abdominal muscles. The Kegelcisor: shaped like a barbell with large, medium and small balls and 7-inches in sterile stainless steel. The Kegelmaster 2000: shaped like a small rod, it has fifteen progressive levels of muscle resistance FPT: shaped like an hourglass and mad4e of surgical stainless steel, it comes with an instruction video, progress chart and hundreds of Kegel exercises tips. You can find all of these products online in most of the sex shops listed in the chapter *Erotic Accessories*.

6) *Betty's Barbell*: this effective pussy exerciser-device, was designed by clever Sexologist Betty Dodson, author of the revolutionary book on masturbation: '*Sex for One*'. You can

find both the Barbell and the book it at www.bettydodson.com and www.babeland.com.

Talking Dirty: Most men love dirty talk during, as well as before any sexual interlude and they pretty much like it any time in-between! Learn to let loose and speak foul when he's fucking you. Find out what he likes to hear, and spill it in his ear. Tell him raunchy stories about your kinky fantasies or what you used to do with boys when you were in high school. It'll drive him wild. Purchase '*The Art of Erotic Talk*.'

Uninhibited: when you learn to enlighten yourself and let loose and *Fuck him for Pleasure*, you'll never go back to feeling that your romantic relationship is stuck forever in neutral. Being uninhibited with him in the bedroom and beyond is so wonderful - it's like a zillion tax-free dollars in your Hope Chest.

Veracity: resolutely accepting that the only thing you can ever candy-coat when it comes to fucking a man, is his cock - will be your first success to fucking a man *from his perspective* and finally getting what you need, want, desire and require back from him, in your romantic relationship.

Wet Dreams: yes, women have them too. When you awake in the middle of the night and your panties are soaked from that sexy dream you've had, it's a lovely feeling, isn't it?

XXX: pornography doesn't exploit women; Ultra-Conservatives who tell you what to think and how to behave are what/who exploit you. Porn is for fantasy, not reality. Furthermore, pornography is absolute proof of how far men will go just to see pussy. So, given that fact, who is in control? **You**. And BTW - if porn is sooooo bad for you, then why are sooooo many Conservatives *always* caught doing something that involves being naked????

Yummies: any sexual or imaginative thing you use, that adds to your sex life and improves the quantity and quality of your romantic relationship. Doesn't matter what it is - if it's something that you want to add for his and your mutual gratification - do it!

Zones: his lovely body is a map of nerves all strung out and circulatory-direct to his cock. Make him moan with a few good sucks and licks anywhere on his zone. You'll be The Goddess. Promise!

Artwork featured at: www.gradiva.com

Creative Screwing

danceforhimnakedlickhisballsvideotapeyourpussywearpastiesdancefor
himnakedlickhisballsvideotapeyourpussywearpastiesdanceforhimnaked
lickhisballsvideotapeyourpussywearpastiesdanceforhimnakedlickhisb
allsvideotapeyourpussywearpastiesdanceforhimnakedlickhisballsvide
otapeyourpussywearpastiesdanceforhimnakedlickhisballsvideotapeyou
rpussywearpastiesdanceforhimnakedlickhisballsvideotapeyourpussywe
arpastiesdanceforhimnakedlickhisballsvideotapeyourpussywearpastie
sdanceforhimnakedlickhisballsvideotapeyourpussywearpastiesdancefo
rhimnakedlickhisballsvideotapeyourpussywearpastiesdanceforhimnake
dlickhisballsvideotapeyourpussywearpastiesdanceforhimnakedlickhis
ballsvideotapeyourpussywearpastiesdanceforhimnakedlickhisballsvid
eotapeyourpussywearpastiesdanceforhimnakedlickhisballsvideotapeyo
urpussywearpastiesdanceforhimnakedlickhisballsvideotapeyourpussyw
earpastiesdanceforhimnakedlickhisballsvideotapeyourpussywearpasti
esdanceforhimnakedlickhisballsvideotapeyourpussywearpastiesdancef
orhimnakedlickhisballsvideotapeyourpussywearpastiesdanceforhimnak
edlickhisballsvideotapeyourpussywearpastiesdanceforhimnakedlickhi
sballsvideotapeyourpussywearpastiesdanceforhimnakedlickhisballsvi
deotapeyourpussywearpastiesdanceforhimnakedlickhisballsvideotapey
ourpussywearpastiesdanceforhimnakedlickhisballsvideotapeyourpussy

Extra Points

wearpastiesdanceforhimnakedlickhisballsvideotapeyourpussywearpast
iesdanceforhimnakedlickhisballsvideotapeyourpussywearpastiesdance
forhimnakedlickhisballsvideotapeyourpussywearpastiesdanceforhimna
kedlickhisballsvideotapeyourpussywearpastiesdanceforhimnakedlickh
isballsvideotapeyourpussywearpastiesdanceforhimnakedlickhisballsv
ideotapeyourpussywearpastiesdanceforhimnakedlickhisballsvideotape
yourpussywearpastiesdanceforhimnakedlickhisballsvideotapeyourpuss
ywearpastiesdanceforhimnakedlickhisballsvideotapeyourpussywearpas
tiesdanceforhimnakedlickhisballsvideotapeyourpussywearpastiesdanc
eforhimnakedlickhisballsvideotapeyourpussywearpastiesdanceforhimn
akedlickhisballsvideotapeyourpussywearpastiesdanceforhimnakedlick
hisballsvideotapeyourpussywearpastiesdanceforhimnakedlickhisballs
videotapeyourpussywearpastiesdanceforhimnakedlickhisballsvideotap
eyourpussywearpastiesdanceforhimnakedlickhisballsvideotapeyourpus
sywearpastiesdanceforhimnakedlickhisballsvideotapeyourpussywearpa
stiesdanceforhimnakedlickhisballsvideotapeyourpussywearpastiesdan
ceforhimnakedlickhisballsvideotapeyourpussywearpastiesdanceforhim
nakedlickhisballsvideotapeyourpussywearpastiesdanceforhimnakedlic
khisballsvideotapeyourpussywearpastiesdanceforhimnakedlickhisball
svideotapeyourpussywearpastiesdanceforhimnakedlickhisballsvideota
peyourpussywearpastiesdanceforhimnakedlickhisballsvideotapeyourpu
ssywearpastiesdanceforhimnakedlickhisballsvideotapeyourpussywearp
astiesdanceforhimnakedlickhisballsvideotapeyourpussywearpastiesda
nceforhimnakedlickhisballsvideotapeyourpussywearpastiesdanceforhi
mnakedlickhisballsvideotapeyourpussywearpastiesdanceforhimnakedli
ckhisballsvideotapeyourpussywearpastiesdanceforhimnakedlickhisbal
lsvideotapeyourpussywearpastiesdanceforhimnakedlickhisballsvideot
apeyourpussywearpastiesdanceforhimnakedlickhisballsvideotapeyourp
ussywearpastiesdanceforhimnakedlickhisballsvideotapeyourpussywear
pastiesdanceforhimnakedlickhisballsvideotapeyourpussywearpastiesd
anceforhimnakedlickhisballsvideotapeyourpussywearpastiesdanceforh
imnakedlickhisballsvideotapeyourpussywearpastiesdanceforhimnakedl
ickhisballsvideotapeyourpussywearpastiesdanceforhimnakedlickhisba
llsvideotapeyourpussywearpastiesdanceforhimnakedlickhisballsvideo
tapeyourpussywearpastiesdanceforhimnakedlickhisballsvideotapeyour

XVI. Extra Points

*One hour of right-down love is worth
an age of dully living on.*

~~~Aphra Behn

Artwork featured at: www.gradiva.com

There isn't any credible or viable excuse for allowing the sexual connection in your romantic relationship to dissipate or reach an expiration date.

Fucking your man must be a *priority,* and if it isn't or it hasn't been, by now you should understand why all, or nearly all, of the intimacy has gone out of your romantic relationship.

Most women have children, work long hours and battle a sink full of dirty dishes - so you *are not special,* nor are you *any exception* to the rule. If you can find a way to balance all the chaos in your life, as well as stretch a dollar bill, then you can manage to arrange some down-time-fucking and regularly make your man feel like a million bucks.

Nearly all of the sexually-inventive ideas that are suggested below can effortlessly be incorporated into your very busy life. All you have to do is *make the effort and want to*:

*Straddle him backward and then move slightly forward so that your ass is aligned and thrusting in his line of vision. Wrap your hands round his feet, and just as he is cuming, gently squeeze and then lightly pull both of his big toes straight.

*Sweeten your vaginal juices by drinking lots of apple, orange, pineapple and cranberry juice throughout the day. When you have sex later that night, your pussy will taste like a Tropical cocktail.

*Walk around the house in his favorite sports jersey and no panties.

*Rent, or better yet purchase, the videos/DVDs for all five seasons of the BBC's hit sitcom *'Coupling'* - the show is full of wonderful perspectives on sex and relationships: it is raunchy, imaginative, naughty and down-right hilarious - with the bonus that your man will enjoy watching it with you! You can find *'Coupling'* for purchase at www.bbcamerica.com.

*Know anything about *Roping-Sex*? No, not tie-up sex - *Mioplex Sex*! Get online and go to www.mioplex.com, then purchase the supplement from Boland Naturals, Inc. called *Mioplex*. *Mioplex* triggers multiple and intensified orgasms in men... much like the effect of skipping rocks in a pond. It will teach your man the *Ropes of enhanced sex* - you will love the ride and he will cum with zeal!

*Always make sure that you have his favorite after-sex goodies on-hand - foods such as: hot wings, cold/frozen pizza, chocolate chips cookies, potato chips, beer. If you are his wife, his live-in fiancée or his live-in girlfriend, continuing to do this deed for him will make it more extraordinary for him because this sort of romantic kindness regularly fades away after a relationship bonds and settles down.

*Wear nothing but a pair of red thigh-high boots, red cowboy boots or red spiked-heels to bed.

*Write down your favorite one-on-one sexual fantasies from 1-to-10, the have him write down his favorite one-on-one sexual fantasies from 1-to-10 - cut-out them out, fold-up each one and ask him to pick a number. Then do it with him.

*Rent a stack of triple XXX porn for a stay-in weekend at home, or when the two of you are headed somewhere out-of-town - you can even take the TV/DVD player on a camping trip! Make a bet with him to see which one of you can keep-up with the actors or which one of you can outlast the other partner. Loser cooks a fancy, romantic meal for two... or you can come up with an even better prize on your own!

*Leave your scent behind by lightly spraying your perfume on his bed pillows while he is in the shower, so that when you're not there the next time he goes to bed, he'll fantasize about you when he touches his cock.

*Meet him at the door dressed in one of the sexy outfits mentioned in the chapter *Erotic Accessories*.

*Rent a speed boat, a row boat, a sail boat or a canoe: take off your pretty panties and fuck him in the middle of the brook, canal, lagoon, lake, ocean, river, or stream. He'll love it!

*Hide one of your sexy thongs or a naughty love note in his suitcase or briefcase the next time he has to go on a business trip or will be in a long, boring meeting.

*Wear your favorite cut-offs, sans panties. Make sure he watches you slide them on before you walk out the door to do your errands.

*Take the back-seats in a movie theater and affectionately play with him in the dark by brushing your fingers against the inside of his thighs and rubbing your palms against his cock over the outside of his jeans.

*Never go to bed without sex just because the two of you are having an argument. Lay that boy on the bed and fuck out your frustration on him until his body is exhausted and flaccid. You win!

*Give him a *Happy Ending Massage*: rub him from neck-to-heel, head-to-toe, and then finish him off with a well-lubricated hand job.

*Ask him how he wants it just as he slides his cock inside of you: does his want your sweet talk or your dirty fantasies?

*Tell him you want to worship him... then slither your tongue into the rim of his delicious derriere.

*Hand him your digital camera and tell him to take pictures of you sucking his cock and licking his balls. Print the pictures off your computer and put them in his sock/underwear drawer.

*Learn to speak sexy sentences in foreign languages such as Russian, French, Italian or Spanish - and master the accents by checking-out tapes from your local library. Surprise him with your chic sex-talk on a special evening of your choice.

*Send him roses with a naughty note written in French - it'll drive him crazy wondering what you said!

*While he is fucking you in the *Missionary Position*, move your hand between his stomach and yours, then slide your fingers in and around the shaft of his cock and your clit as he moves inside you. It's a wonderful visual for him, and it will feel sooooooo incredible for you.

*Make sure you gently touch his cock during a private moment, at least once-a-day at any time that neither one of you are 'in the mood', and when there is no opportunity for a sex-tryst. This works especially well in situations such as: a time when you're in traffic after a hellish day of holiday shopping; or the kids are crabby and snappish after a long vacation day at the beach; or he's just found-out his critical boss wants extra work done on a report. When you touch and connect with your man's cock in this way, it makes him feel wanted, needed, and loved.

*Go online to www.store.Playboy.com, and purchase a replica of the original *Playboy Club Bunny Costume*. Put it on and serve him his favorite drink. Then ask him what he'd like as an appetizer before dinner.

*Text-message him and tell him that his naughty-boy ass is going to catch it the next time you get him naked.

*Massage his entire body with your hair.

*Have a real tussle with him in bed by creating your own personal wrestling arena! You can order the *Romance Wrestling Arena*: it has four ring posts, four base plates and lots of red rope. Think of how much better your arguments will be with both of you naked in a wrestling ring! Go online right now and purchase this ingenious idea from www.romancewrestling.com.

*After he's just gotten out of a hot shower or bath, lead him to the bed and have a make-out party with his cock and with his balls. *Passionately kiss his cock and his balls all over*. The heat from the shower will have brought the blood to his cock and his balls, and the friction of your lips kissing him like that is a sweet sensation he will be indebted to have experienced from you.

*Purchase a large, fake-fur mink blanket. Here's what you do with it: Lay it on the floor, position him comfortably on the blanket on all fours, then slide beneath him and suck his cock. Ask him to cum on your face. (Note: just keep your eyes closed as he cums, because if you get any of his cum in your eyes, it'll give you red eye!)

Niagara in the little blue bottle will cause a lovely splash in your libido the next time you fuck him. The drink works as an aphrodisiac, and many woman testify that they've experienced everything from: a warm, tingly feeling in their genitals; becoming downright horny; a hot-blooded rush! Get it at www.littlebluebottle.com.

*Give him a *Shadow Striptease* by placing a lighted lamp behind a large cardboard triangle, so that it will cast your shadow on a wall. Put on the sort of music he likes, and move your body in a smooth, seductive manner, so that he sees only your shadow and not you.

*Leave a sexy, cryptic message for him with his assistant.

Always, always, always wax, shave or depilate your pussy. Men love the look, feel, smell and taste of smooth.

*Make-up your own erotic stories in bed or read to him from Letters to Penthouse or Forum Stories. It will render him horny and sex-crazed.

*Shoot a home-video/DVD of yourself with your camcorder while you masturbate, and when he gets home from work or school or a night out with the boys, hand him his favorite drink then give him his own private showing in the bedroom.

*On a hot afternoon while he's washing the car, lean against the hood, take the hose and let the water gush over your body. Wear something see-through!

*Go to his office or his job on an afternoon that you know he'll be in a monotonous meeting. Tell his assistant you need to speak with him about something important. When he takes you into his office or to a backroom for some privacy, lay face down on his desk or pull-up your skirt and lean against the wall: tell him you just couldn't wait until later for him to fuck you and would he please do you *now*!

*Body paint him in edible chocolate paints.

*After you've given him a hand-job, wrap your hair around his cock so he can cum in it.

*Meet him at the front door on a day when no one else is home and before he has the chance to say a word, unzip his jeans and give him great Head.

*Next time his issue of *Playboy* magazine arrives in the mail, ask a girlfriend to take some digital snapshots of you posing naked in a variety of sexy positions: use all sorts of props, lingerie or ideas from the chapter *Erotic Accessories*. Print-out black-and-white and color 8'10's shots of your favorite photographs off your computer printer, and then glue the naked photos of you to any *advertisement page* in his *Playboy* magazine. Give him the magazine and tell him that you think he'll find one of the models very pleasurable to look at.

*Leave a red-lipstick trail of kisses all over his body.

*Purchase a psychedelic 'black' light that is used in nightclubs. White glows brilliant in this type of lighting. Brush your body with white or florescent body glitter, and then fuck him in this harem-type atmosphere.

*Purchase a mini-tape recorder and secretly tape your next sexual liaison with him. Hand it to him on his way out the door so that he can listen to it on his way to work.

*You should have a clear idea by now what sort of kinky things turn your man on. Take a digital photograph of you doing something kinky-n-spicy that will make his singe to fuck you; cut the photograph into a jigsaw, and give him a big-boy puzzle.

*Ask him to masturbate for you - tell him to cum on your breasts, and then lick his cock clean.

*On a tranquil evening, use your Venus razor to smoothly shave-off all his pubic hair, and then give him sensuous oil Cock Massage from the entire base of his cock, to the underneath of his balls. All the nerve-endings in his skin will be alive and tingling and when he cums, it will be an extraordinary sensation.

*Have a *Come-Hither* wardrobe of sexy clothing, visually pleasurable costumes, colorful lingerie and naughty-goody items just for sex, because of him.

*Contact any of the brothels in the State of Nevada, such as *The Chicken Ranch,* and ask the business office to please mail you one of their commercial-trade sex-menus. On an evening when you both have a lot of time for some fun, put a red-light in a bedroom lamp and throw-around satin pillows and soft, colorful blankets, then hand him the sex-menu and tell him you'll give him his lay-of-choice. Offer him the complete Brothel treatment!

*Thrill his male ego by ordering a do-it-yourself, custom made *Make Your One Dildo Kit* from www.goodvibrations.com and have him model so you can construct the perfect dildo molded from his exquisite hard cock.

*Purchase the '*How to Strip for Your Man*' video/DVD from www.calston.com, featuring expert striptease artist, Gio. Gio will show you how to highlight your best, sexiest features and she'll give you the keys to self-confidence and spontaneity while dancing naked.

*Take him to your local Adult Toy Store. Ask him to buy whatever naughty plaything he wants.

*Fill paper bags with sand and put large scented candles in them, then line the hallway or staircase with the bags in a trail to anywhere in the house that you want him to find you, and then turn off all the house lights: 1) have a passion picnic set up in the bedroom where you can feed each other finger-food 2) position a bear rug in front of the fireplace and bring massage oil for a fantastic fuck 3) be in a bubble bath with champagne and a rubber ducky for a seductive liaison. 4) Come-up with your own ideas!

*Rent a room in a seedy hotel, view the filthy movies and then fuck him like you're the whore and he's your client. This is an excellent time and place for him to ass-fuck you.

*After you've waxed your pussy, dress in pink BabyDoll panties and tie your hair in ponytails or braids; then tell him you're his naughty little girl and you need to be punished.

*Masturbate for him with a long-neck beer bottle or a Popsicle.

*After you've performed a real cock-achingly slow striptease for him, wiggle out of your panties and dip the crotch in his beer mug, and then wring the beer-soaked panties into his panting mouth.

*Offer him an entire weekend of '9½ *Weeks*.'

*Purchase the books '*Forbidden French*' and '*Forbidden Italian*' and bone-up on spicy words from abroad.

*Lightly massage the pathway between his cock and his anus until he screams that he's going to explode from the titillating pleasure.

*Massage his entire body, head-to-toe and neck-to-heel, only with the tips of your fingers.

*You should own: ~a pair of crotch-less panties~ ~a comfortable pair of handcuffs~ ~a flat-ended riding crop~ ~a leather blindfold~ ~a fancy garter-belt and garter~ ~Ben Wa balls~ ~satin sheets~ ~Bindi jewels~.

*Manipulate the upper part of his heel, just below the Achilles tendon and watch-out for his unexpected sexual response. Just as I showed you in the chapter '*Your Man's Undisclosed Moan Zones*', his entire body is a simmering volcano of sexual eruption - fool around with his Moan Zones often.

*Make the *Shower Suck* a Sunday tradition. Men crave consistency.

*Temporary tattoo his name on your ass. Or Left Nipple. Or in the inside of your thighs.

*Let him know how much you love the way he re-defines the term 'eating-out'. The more encouragement he gets from you on his oral sex skills, the more enthusiastic he will be to please you that way.

*Go to www.annieSprinkle.com, and read-up on how to get into her *One Woman Sex Show* or her *Goddess and Sluts Seminars*. She is wonderful! Annie Sprinkle will re-train your brain to what a delightful sex life you can have if you will just see yourself as men see you.

*Here's what men get at topless bars and clubs: 1) lingerie modeling 2) oil and mud wrestling brawls between a cluster of girls 3) stripper contests 4) banana and cherry eating contests 5) Silhouette dancing 6) Go-Go Dancing 7) Dancing girls on: stages, couches, tables, pedestals 8) Dancing girls in: laps, showers, cages 9) Foxy Boxing 10) Burlesque Dancing 11) Fantasy Costume Dancing 12) Girly pillow fights... and $8.00 for a warm beer! If you want to know how to put on a real sex show for your man, go into any topless bar/club, ask if you can watch a few of the stripper shows, and then get some real seduction tips from a dancer.

*In bed, read him the novel 'Exit to Eden' by authoress Anne Rice. Bring along a vibrator.

*Go to www.masqueradebooks.com and ask them to send you one of the naughtiest dirty book catalogues on the market.

*Rent a few of these sexy, passionate films on video/DVD and have a night of Adult Fantasy Flicks, complete with man-hungry finger foods and flowing beer:

1) *Wild Orchid* 2) *Wild Orchid II: Shades of Blue* 3) *Sliver* 4) *Hot Spot* 5) *Henry and June* 6) *Animal Instinct* 7) *Back Stab* 8) *After Dark* 9) *Night Eyes* 10) *Whispers in the Dark* 11) *No Way out* 12) *The Big Easy* 13) *Body of Evidence* 14) *Damage* 15) *Body Heat* 16) *Blue Velvet* 17) *White Palace* 18) *Sea of Love* 19) *Angel Heart* 20) *Another Woman's Lipstick* 21) *Red Shoe Diaries* 22) *Fatal Attraction* 23) *Body Double* 24) *Basic Instinct* 25) *Indecent Behavior* 26) *Sexual Responses* 27) *Body Chemistry* 28)*Body Chemistry II* 29) *9 ½ Weeks* 30) *Out of Sight.*

*Betty Dobson is the authoress of the sexually ground-breaking book 'Sex for One'. She also has Masturbation Seminars where she teaches woman how and where to touch themselves, so that women can learn how to orgasm. She also teaches women the difference between Clit and Vaginal orgasms. If you'd like to know more about the extensive sexual potential of your body, please go online and visit www.bettydobson.com.

*Pour his favorite beer all over your body and ask him to suck it off.

*Want to write him a sexy letter, but can't find the right words? Then go to www.instantsexyletters.com, and purchase their Instant sexy Letters kit! It's a great idea for women who are really shy, tongue-tied or unsure of how to say it to their man.

*Want to find the best Sex Everything? Then go online to www.janesguide.com, where they critique the complete sex industry, from erotica writings and nude photography, to xxx porno. If you want to become more comfortable with becoming his sex object, the site will also give you online addresses and links to other internet sites that feature "girl-next-door" photos, vintage pin-up girls and glamour nudes. One of my best friends, Giovanna, had a glamour semi-nude, black-and-white photo taken for her husband for Valentine's Day. Just seeing that picture on his dresser gives her a sex-shot-of-confidence boost every day. You have everything it takes to be sexually confident; all you need to do is explore your own imagination.

*Smell is the most powerful aphrodisiacs in the world, and that Fact comes from the Smell & Taste Treatment and Research Foundation in Chicago, Illinois. The aroma combination of cinnamon-pumpkin pie and lavender increases blood flow to a man's cock. So, all you have to do is bake a cinnamon-pumpkin pie and spray a little lavender around the house, and he'll be yanking down your panties. For more information on the aphrodisiac of smell, read Alan Hirsch book, 'Scentsational Sex'!

*If you are in a committed relationship, always tell him that you love him after he makes you come. (This will tie-in the sweet romance with the raw fucking).

*If you are in a very new relationship, always tell him how creative he is after he has made you come. (This sets-up a good habit for later on in the relationship).

Rid your essence of relationship boredom by making many of your sexual encounters with him unique, creative and imaginative.

Artwork featured at: www.gradiva.com

Great sex is loaded with intense, subconscious communications... it's the cement of the man-woman bond. If you let that go... it's the beginning of the end.

~~~Dr. Ava Cadell

Nannette LaRee Hernandez

TheDirtyGirlsAClockworkOrangeEasyRiderLastTangoinParisTheDirtyGir
lsAClockworkOrangeEasyRiderLastTangoinParisTheDirtyGirlsAClockwor
kOrangeEasyRiderLastTangoinParisTheDirtyGirlsAClockworkOrangeEasy
RiderLastTangoinParisTheDirtyGirlsAClockworkOrangeEasyRiderLastTa
ngoinParisTheDirtyGirlsAClockworkOrangeEasyRiderLastTangoinParisT
heDirtyGirlsAClockworkOrangeEasyRiderLastTangoinParisTheDirtyGirl
sAClockworkOrangeEasyRiderLastTangoinParisTheDirtyGirlsAClockwork
OrangeEasyRiderLastTangoinParisTheDirtyGirlsAClockworkOrangeEasyR
iderLastTangoinParisTheDirtyGirlsAClockworkOrangeEasyRiderLastTan
goinParisTheDirtyGirlsAClockworkOrangeEasyRiderLastTangoinParisTh
eDirtyGirlsAClockworkOrangeEasyRiderLastTangoinParisTheDirtyGirls

Erotica In The Movies: The List

AClockworkOrangeEasyRiderLastTangoinParisTheDirtyGirlsAClockworkO
rangeEasyRiderLastTangoinParisTheDirtyGirlsAClockworkOrangeEasyRi
derLastTangoinParisTheDirtyGirlsAClockworkOrangeEasyRiderLastTang
oinParisTheDirtyGirlsAClockworkOrangeEasyRiderLastTangoinParisThe
DirtyGirlsAClockworkOrangeEasyRiderLastTangoinParisTheDirtyGirlsA
ClockworkOrangeEasyRiderLastTangoinParisTheDirtyGirlsAClockworkOr
angeEasyRiderLastTangoinParisTheDirtyGirlsAClockworkOrangeEasyRid
erLastTangoinParisTheDirtyGirlsAClockworkOrangeEasyRiderLastTango
inParisTheDirtyGirlsAClockworkOrangeEasyRiderLastTangoinParisTheD
irtyGirlsAClockworkOrangeEasyRiderLastTangoinParisTheDirtyGirlsAC
lockworkOrangeEasyRiderLastTangoinParisTheDirtyGirlsAClockworkOra
ngeEasyRiderLastTangoinParisTheDirtyGirlsAClockworkOrangeEasyRide
rLastTangoinParisTheDirtyGirlsAClockworkOrangeEasyRiderLastTangoi
nParisTheDirtyGirlsAClockworkOrangeEasyRiderLastTangoinParisTheDi
rtyGirlsAClockworkOrangeEasyRiderLastTangoinParisTheDirtyGirlsACl
ockworkOrangeEasyRiderLastTangoinParisTheDirtyGirlsAClockworkOran
geEasyRiderLastTangoinParisTheDirtyGirlsAClockworkOrangeEasyRider
LastTangoinParisTheDirtyGirlsAClockworkOrangeEasyRiderLastTangoin
ParisTheDirtyGirlsAClockworkOrangeEasyRiderLastTangoinParisTheDir
tyGirlsAClockworkOrangeEasyRiderLastTangoinParisTheDirtyGirlsAClo
ckworkOrangeEasyRiderLastTangoinParisTheDirtyGirlsAClockworkOrang
eEasyRiderLastTangoinParisTheDirtyGirlsAClockworkOrangeEasyRiderL
astTangoinParisTheDirtyGirlsAClockworkOrangeEasyRiderLastTangoinP
arisTheDirtyGirlsAClockworkOrangeEasyRiderLastTangoinParisTheDirt
yGirlsAClockworkOrangeEasyRiderLastTangoinParisTheDirtyGirlsACloc
kworkOrangeEasyRiderLastTangoinParisTheDirtyGirlsAClockworkOrange
EasyRiderLastTangoinParisTheDirtyGirlsAClockworkOrangeEasyRiderLa
stTangoinParisTheDirtyGirlsAClockworkOrangeEasyRiderLastTangoinPa
risTheDirtyGirlsAClockworkOrangeEasyRiderLastTangoinParisTheDirty
GirlsAClockworkOrangeEasyRiderLastTangoinParisTheDirtyGirlsAClock
workOrangeEasyRiderLastTangoinParisTheDirtyGirlsAClockworkOrangeE
asyRiderLastTangoinParisTheDirtyGirlsAClockworkOrangeEasyRiderLas
tTangoinParisTheDirtyGirlsAClockworkOrangeEasyRiderLastTangoinPar
isTheDirtyGirlsAClockworkOrangeEasyRiderLastTangoinParisTheDirtyG
irlsAClockworkOrangeEasyRiderLastTangoinParisTheDirtyGirlsAClockw
orkOrangeEasyRiderLastTangoinParisTheDirtyGirlsAClockworkOrangeEa
syRiderLastTangoinParisTheDirtyGirlsAClockworkOrangeEasyRiderLast
TangoinParisTheDirtyGirlsAClockworkOrangeEasyRiderLastTangoinPari
sTheDirtyGirlsAClockworkOrangeEasyRiderLastTangoinParisTheDirtyGi
rlsAClockworkOrangeEasyRiderLastTangoinParisTheDirtyGirlsAClockwo
rkOrangeEasyRiderLastTangoinParisTheDirtyGirlsAClockworkOrangeEas
yRiderLastTangoinParisTheDirtyGirlsAClockworkOrangeEasyRiderLastT
angoinParisTheDirtyGirlsAClockworkOrangeEasyRiderLastTangoinParis

XVII. Erotica In The Movies: The List

Artwork featured at: www.gradiva.com

Taken from the website, www.jahsonic.com, the following movie list from foreign films to short flicks, is a great place to start when searching for a hot film to watch with your man.

•1896
The Kiss (1896) - William Heise

•1897
Douche Après le Bain (1897) - Louis Lumière

•1913
Traffic in Souls (1913) - George Loane Tucker

•1914
Damaged Goods (1914)

•1915
A Fool There Was (1915) -Frank Powell
A Free Ride (1915)
Inspiration (1915) - George Platt

•1916
The Sex Lure (1916)

•1917
The Tiger Woman (1917)
Cleopatra (1917)

•1919
Male and Female (1919) - Cecil B. DeMille
Opium (1919) - Robert Dinesen

•1920
The Tree of Knowledge (1920)

•1921
The Sheik (1921) -starring Valentino

•1922
Blood and Sand (1922) -starring Valentino

•1925
The Merry Widow (1925) - Erich von Stroheim

•1926
Son of the Sheik (1926) -starring Valentino

•1927
It (1927) - Josef von Sternberg, Clarence G. Badger
Hula (1927) Clara Bow

•1928
Un Chien Andalou (1928)
Pandora's Box (1928)

•1929
Haxan (Witchcraft Through the Ages) (1929)
Queen Kelly (1929) - Erich von Stroheim

•1930
L'Age d'Or (1930) - Luis Bunuel
The Blue Angel (1930) - Josef von Sternberg
Madam Satan (1930) - Cecil B. De Mille

•1931
Tabu: A Story of the South Seas (1931) - F.W. Murnau

•1932
Extase (1932) - Gustav Machatý

•1933
Queen Christina (1933) - starring Greta Garbo
42nd Street (1933)
The Devil is a Woman (1935) - Josef von Sternberg

•1937
Damaged Goods (1937) - Phil Goldstone

•1942
Sex Hygiene (1942) - Otto Brower, John Ford

•1945
Mom and Dad (1945) - William Beaudine

•1947
Anger 1 (1947) - Kenneth Anger

•1950
Un Chant d'Amour (1950)

•1953
Summer With Monika (1953)

•1955
Garden of Eden (1955)

•1956
And God Created Woman - (1956)

•1957
I Vampiri (1957)

•1959
The Immoral Mr. Teas (1959)

•1960
Peeping Tom (1960)
The Virgin Spring (1960)

•1961
Victim (1961)

•1962
Jules and Jim (1962)
Knife in the Water (1962)
Lolita (1962)

•1963
Flaming Creatures (1963)
Tystnaden/The Silence (1963)
Contempt (1963)
The Servant (1963)

•1964
Sexus (1964)
The Dirty Girls (1964)

•1965
I, A Woman (1965)
Repulsion (1965)
Faster Pussycat Kill Kill (1965)
The Alley Cats (1965)

•1966
Persona (1966)
Hugs and Kisses (1967)
Blow-Up (1966)

•1967
Belle de Jour (1967)
Yellow/Blue (1967)

•1968
Teorema (1968)
Barbarella (1968)
Histoires Extraordinaires aka Spirits of The Dead (1968)
If... (1968)
Therese und Isabell (1968)

•1969
Easy Rider (1969)
Femina Ridens- The Frightened Woman (1969)
The Libertine (1969)
Kärlekens språk/Language of Love (1969)

•1970
Performance (1970)
The Lickerish Quartet (1970)
Trash (1970)
Women In Love (1970)
Pornography in Denmark (1970)
Why? (1970)
Stille dage i Clichy/Quiet Days in Clichy (1970)
Mona (1970)

•1971
Klute (1971)
The Devils (1971)
History of the Blue Movie (1971)

•1972
Deep Throat (1972)
The Bitter Tears of Petra von Kant (1972)
Deliverance (1972)
Behind the Green Door (1972)
Last Tango in Paris (1972)
Everything You Always Wanted to Know About Sex But Were Afraid to Ask (1972)
The Canterbury Tales (1972)

•1973
La Grande Bouffe (1973)
Score (1973)
The Mother and the Whore (1973)

•1974
Le Fantôme de la liberté (1974)
Going Places (1974)
The Night Porter (1974)
Wife To Be Sacrificed (1974)
Ilsa - She Wolf of the SS (1974)
Caged Heat (1974)
Sweet Movie (1974)
Emmanuelle (1974)
Il Fiore Delle Mille e Una Notte/Arabian Nights (1974)

•1975
The Story of O (1975)
The Image/The Punishment of Anne (1975)
The First Nudie Musical (1975)
The Beast (1975)

•1976
Salo (1976)
Ai No Corrida/In the Realm of the Senses (1976)
Maitresse (1976)
Je t'aime moi non plus (1976)
Ugly Dirty and Bad (1976)
Inserts (1975)

•1977
Bilitis (1977)
Una Giornata Particolare (1977)
Outrageous (1977)

•1978
La Cage Aux Folles (1978)
Pretty Baby (1978)

•1979
The Brood (1979)
Caligula (1979)

•1980
Dressed to Kill (1980)
Spetters (1980)

•1981
Beau Pere (1981)

Taxi Zum Klo (1981)
Pixote (1981)
Tales of Ordinary Madness (1981)

•1982
Cafe Flesh (1982)
Querelle (1982)

•1983
Videodrome (1983)
Woman in Flames (1983)

•1984
Special Effects (1984)
Tightrope (1984)
Crimes of Passion (1984)
The Company of Wolves (1984)
Body Double (1984)

•1985
Kiss of the Spider Woman (1985)
Tampopo (1985)

•1986
Blue Velvet (1986)
Betty Blue (1986)
Something Wild (1986)
She's Gotta Have It (1986)
9 1/2 Weeks (1986)

•1987
Angel Heart (1987)

•1988
Story of Women (1988)
Tetsuo: The Ironman (1988)
Dangerous Liaisons (1988)
Women on the Verge of a Nervous Breakdown (1988)

•1989
The Cook, the Thief, His Wife and Her Lover (1989)
Mr. Hire (1989)
Sex, Lies and Videotape (1989)

•1990
Henry & June (1990)
¡Átame!/ Tie Me Up! Tie Me Down! (1990)

•1991
My Own Private Idaho (1991) - Gus Van Sant

•1992
Bitter Moon (1992)
Tokyo Decadence (1992)
Damage (1992)
Basic Instinct (1992)

•1993
Boxing Helena (1993)

•1994
The Adventures of Priscilla, Queen of the Desert (1994)

•1995
Wild Side (1995-98)

•1996
Bound (1996)

•1997
Conspirators of Pleasure (1997)

•1998
Fucking Åmål/Show Me Love (1998)
L' Ennui (1998)

•1999
Romance (1999)
Eyes Wide Shut (1999)

•2000
Baise-Moi (2000)

•2001
Intimacy (2001)
Lucía y el Sexo/Sex and Lucia (2001)
Mama Tambien/And Your Mother Too (2001)
The Center of the World (2001)

•2002
Irréversible (2002)
Ken Park (2002)

•2003
In the Cut (2003)
The Dreamers (2003)
Swimming Pool (2003)

•2004
Ma Mère (2004)
9 songs (2004)

Sex in Films, by Babette White... this mesmerizing book is jam-packed with photographs and information, from the obscure film shorts to the well-known films from both Hollywood and foreign countries. Every photograph provides a short caption identifying the motion picture, and the book is divided into chapters of sexual predilection and/or deviation. Each chapter describes every era of filmmaking and the disputes with the censors, ranging from the early 1920's to the Now.

 One Hundred Sex Scenes, by Neal Fulwood... will put you in the mood for the movies, and prove just how much Hollywood sets the paradigm for Society. Each chapter takes a movie, and demonstrates how 'the sex scene' was the crucial statement that gave the movie thrust.

I mean, don't you ever really wanna be pounded hard, you know, like when the bed is moving all around and it's all sweaty and your head is knocking up against the headboard and you feel like it might just blow off. Dammit, I just really wanna be fucked, you know just really fucked!

~~~Charlotte, *Sex and the City*

Artwork featured at: *www.gradiva.com*

251

Creative Screwing

readreadreadreadreadreadreadreadreadreadreadreadreadreadreadr
eadreadreadreadreadreadreadreadreadreadreadreadreadreadreadre
adreadreadreadreadreadreadreadreadreadreadreadreadreadreadrea
dreadreadreadreadreadreadreadreadreadreadreadreadreadreadread
readreadreadreadreadreadreadreadreadreadreadreadreadreadreadr
eadreadreadreadreadreadreadreadreadreadreadreadreadreadreadre
adreadreadreadreadreadreadreadreadreadreadreadreadreadreadrea
dreadreadreadreadreadreadreadreadreadreadreadreadreadreadread
readreadreadreadreadreadreadreadreadreadreadreadreadreadreadr
eadreadreadreadreadreadreadreadreadreadreadreadreadreadreadre
adreadreadreadreadreadreadreadreadreadreadreadreadreadreadrea
dreadreadreadreadreadreadreadreadreadreadreadreadreadreadread

Bibliography & Outstanding Booklist

Readreadreadreadreadreadreadreadreadreadreadreadreadreadreadr
eadreadreadreadreadreadreadreadreadreadreadreadreadreadreadre
adreadreadreadreadreadreadreadreadreadreadreadreadreadreadrea
dreadreadreadreadreadreadreadreadreadreadreadreadreadreadread
readreadreadreadreadreadreadreadreadreadreadreadreadreadreadr
eadreadreadreadreadreadreadreadreadreadreadreadreadreadreadre
adreadreadreadreadreadreadreadreadreadreadreadreadreadreadrea
dreadreadreadreadreadreadreadreadreadreadreadreadreadreadread
readreadreadreadreadreadreadreadreadreadreadreadreadreadreadr
eadreadreadreadreadreadreadreadreadreadreadreadreadreadreadre
adreadreadreadreadreadreadreadreadreadreadreadreadreadreadrea
dreadreadreadreadreadreadreadreadreadreadreadreadreadreadread
readreadreadreadreadreadreadreadreadreadreadreadreadreadreadr
eadreadreadreadreadreadreadreadreadreadreadreadreadreadreadre
adreadreadreadreadreadreadreadreadreadreadreadreadreadreadrea
dreadreadreadreadreadreadreadreadreadreadreadreadreadreadread
readreadreadreadreadreadreadreadreadreadreadreadreadreadreadr
eadreadreadreadreadreadreadreadreadreadreadreadreadreadreadre
adreadreadreadreadreadreadreadreadreadreadreadreadreadreadrea
dreadreadreadreadreadreadreadreadreadreadreadreadreadreadread
readreadreadreadreadreadreadreadreadreadreadreadreadreadreadr
eadreadreadreadreadreadreadreadreadreadreadreadreadreadreadre
adreadreadreadreadreadreadreadreadreadreadreadreadreadreadrea
dreadreadreadreadreadreadreadreadreadreadreadreadreadreadread
readreadreadreadreadreadreadreadreadreadreadreadreadreadreadr
eadreadreadreadreadreadreadreadreadreadreadreadreadreadreadre
adreadreadreadreadreadreadreadreadreadreadreadreadreadreadrea
dreadreadreadreadreadreadreadreadreadreadreadreadreadreadread
readreadreadreadreadreadreadreadreadreadreadreadreadreadreadr
eadreadreadreadreadreadreadreadreadreadreadreadreadreadreadre
adreadreadreadreadreadreadreadreadreadreadreadreadreadreadrea
dreadreadreadreadreadreadreadreadreadreadreadreadreadreadread
readreadreadreadreadreadreadreadreadreadreadreadreadreadreadr
eadreadreadreadreadreadreadreadreadreadreadreadreadreadreadre
adreadreadreadreadreadreadreadreadreadreadreadreadreadreadrea
dreadreadreadreadreadreadreadreadreadreadreadreadreadreadread

XVIII. Bibliography & Outstanding Booklist

All the books mentioned in my book, can be found at your local bookstore or online at www.amazon.com, www.overstock.com, www.barnesnoble.com, www.half.com, or at most of the sex-related websites featured in each chapter in this book. Should you have trouble locating any of the books that I've featured, simply put the title of the book and the author's name into any Internet Search Engine, such as Yahoo or Goggle, and the website where you can find the book for purchase, will instantly appear.

Read.

What you mentally process and study will greatly improve your sexual, emotional, spiritual and physical relationship with your man.

If I've accidently missed an author from one-of my chapters here in this Bibliography/Booklist, please email me at Seshat65@yahoo.com and I will fix it immediately. A Sex Goddess I am; perfect I shall never be!

Why Adam ate that Apple

Married Love, by Dr. Marie Carmichael Stopes

How To Make Your Man Behave In 21 Days Or Less: Using The Secrets Of Professional Dog Trainers, by Karen Salmansohn

The Bastard on the Couch, edited by Daniel Jones

Brain Sex, by Anne Moir

Your Man's Personal Playmate

The Penis Book, by Joseph Cohen

Dick: A User's Guide, by Michele C. Moore

Sex, the Heart and Erectile Dysfunction, by Graham Jackson

Dick: A Guide to the Penis for Men and Women, by Caroline Da Costa, Michele Moore

Nuclear Head:

Blow Him Away: How to Give Him Mind-Blowing Oral Sex, by Marcy Michaels, Marie Desalle

The Ultimate Guide to Fellatio: How to Go Down on a Man and Give Him Mind-Blowing Pleasure, by Violet Blue

The Idiot's Pocket Guide to Oral Sex, by Ava Cadell

The Dexterity of Bootie Worship:

The Topping Book, by Dossie Easton and Janet W. Hardy

The Bottoming Book, by Dossie Easton and Janet W. Hardy

The Ultimate Guide to Anal Sex for Women, by Tristan Taormino

Anal Health and Pleasure: A Guide for Men and Women, by Jack Morin, M.D.

Naughty Spanking: stories from A to Z, by Lorie Wiseman

Your Personal Bliss:

Vaginas: An Owner's Manual, by Elizabeth Topp, Carol Livoti

Female Ejaculation and the G-Spot, by Deborah Sundahl

The BIG Book of Masturbation, by Martha Cornog

Cosmopolitan: The Nice Girl's Guide to Sensational Sex, By Nancy Kalish

Erotic Accessories

Flogging, by Joseph Bean

The Erotic Bondage Book, by Jay Wiseman

Screw the Roses, Send Me the Thorns: The Romance and Sexual Sorcery of Sadomasochism, by Philip Miller and Molly Devon

When Someone You Love Is Kinky, by Dossie Easton and Catherine A. Liszt

Sensuous Magic, Patrick Califia-Rice

The Ultimate Guide to Sexual Fantasy: How to Turn Your Fantasies into Reality, by Violet Blue

The Many Joys of Sex Toy: The Ultimate How-to Handbook for Couples and Singles, by Anne Semans

Private Dancer

The Japanese Art of Sex: How to Tease, Seduce and Pleasure the Samurai in Your Bedroom, by Jina Bacarr

Little Book of Reflexology, by Michelle R. Kluck-Ebbin

How to Make a Man Fall in Love with You, by Tracy Cabot

Modern Sex Magick, by Donald Michael Kraig

Sex in History, by Reay Tannahill

Seduction: Tempt, Tease and Tantalize Your Lover, by: Snow Raven Starborn

Intercourses: An Aphrodisiac Cookbook, by: Martha Hopkins and Randall Lockridge

Seductress: Women Who Ravished the World and Their Lost Art of Love, by Betsy Prioleau

Love Potions and Charms: Over 50 Ways to Seduce, Bewitch, and Cherish Your Lover, by Frank Melville, G. Ogilvy, Francis Melville

The Goddess Guide to Love: Timeless Secrets to Divine Romance, by Margie Lapanja

How To Be a Sex Goddess, by Sarah Tomczak

The Goddess in the Bedroom: A Passionate Woman's Guide to Celebrating Sexuality Every Night of the Week, by Zsuzsanna E. Budapest

The Complete Idiot's Guide to Being a Sex Goddess, by Stacy Clark and Eve Adamson

Sex Secrets of Escorts, by Veronica Monet

Phone Sex, by Miranda Austin

Down and Dirty Sex Secrets: The New and Naughty Guide to Being Great in Bed, by Tristan Taormino

Kissing School: Seven Lessons on Love, Lips, and Life Force, by Cherie Byrd

The Hedonism Handbook, by Michael Flocker

Sex Tips for Straight Women from a Gay Man, by Dan Anderson and Maggie Berman

The Experts Guide to 100 Things Everyone Should Know How to Do, by Samantha Ettus

The Ultimate Guide to Sex and Disability: For All of Us Who Live With Disabilities, Chronic Pain, and Illness, by Cory Silverburg

Sexual Function in People with Disability and Chronic Illness: a Health Professional's Guide, by Marca L. Sipski

Sex Disasters:And How To Survive Them, by Charles Moser, Ph.D., M.D.

Encyclopedia of Unusual Sex Practices, by Brenda Love

The ABC's of Fucking:

The Art of Kissing, by William Cane

Dirty Talk, by Lynne Stanton and Stanley Chow

The Fine Art Of Erotic Talk: How To Entice, Excite, And Enchant Your Lover With Words, by Bonnie Gabriel

The Kama Sutra For 21st Century Lovers, by Anne Hooper

Kissing: Everything You Ever Wanted to Know About One of Life's Sweetest Pleasures, by Andrea Demirjian

Love Elixirs' Titania's Book of Romantic Potions, by Titania Hardie and Sara Morris

Love Potions: A Guide to Aphrodisiacs and Sexual Pleasure, by Cynthia Mervis Watson, MD

Erotica In The Movies:

Sex in Films, by Babette White

One Hundred Sex Scenes, by Neal Fulwood

eyeofthebeholdereyeofthebeholdereyeofthebeholdereyeofthebeholdere
yeofthebeholdereyeofthebeholdereyeofthebeholdereyeofthebeholderey
eofthebeholdereyeofthebeholdereyeofthebeholdereyeofthebeholdereyo
ofthebeholdereyeofthebeholdereyeofthebeholdereyeofthebeholdereyeo
fthebeholdereyeofthebeholdereyeofthebeholdereyeofthebeholdereyeof
thebeholdereyeofthebeholdereyeofthebeholdereyeofthebeholdereyeoft
hebeholdereyeofthebeholdereyeofthebeholdereyeofthebeholdereyeofth
ebeholdereyeofthebeholdereyeofthebeholdereyeofthebeholdereyeofthe

Divine Photography, Artwork & Illustration

beholdereyeofthebeholdereyeofthebeholdereyeofthebeholdereyeoftheb
eholdereyeofthebeholdereyeofthebeholdereyeofthebeholdereyeofthebe
holdereyeofthebeholdereyeofthebeholdereyeofthebeholdereyeofthebeh
oldereyeofthebeholdereyeofthebeholdereyeofthebeholdereyeofthebeho
ldereyeofthebeholdereyeofthebeholdereyeofthebeholdereyeofthebehol
dereyeofthebeholdereyeofthebeholdereyeofthebeholdereyeofthebehold
ereyeofthebeholdereyeofthebeholdereyeofthebeholdereyeofthebeholde
reyeofthebeholdereyeofthebeholdereyeofthebeholdereyeofthebeholder
eyeofthebeholdereyeofthebeholdereyeofthebeholdereyeofthebeholdere
yeofthebeholdereyeofthebeholdereyeofthebeholdereyeofthebeholderey
eofthebeholdereyeofthebeholdereyeofthebeholdereyeofthebeholdereye
ofthebeholdereyeofthebeholdereyeofthebeholdereyeofthebeholdereyeo
fthebeholdereyeofthebeholdereyeofthebeholdereyeofthebeholdereyeof
thebeholdereyeofthebeholdereyeofthebeholdereyeofthebeholdereyeoft
hebeholdereyeofthebeholdereyeofthebeholdereyeofthebeholdereyeofth
ebeholdereyeofthebeholdereyeofthebeholdereyeofthebeholdereyeofthe
beholdereyeofthebeholdereyeofthebeholdereyeofthebeholdereyeoftheb
eholdereyeofthebeholdereyeofthebeholdereyeofthebeholdereyeofthebe
holdereyeofthebeholdereyeofthebeholdereyeofthebeholdereyeofthebeh
oldereyeofthebeholdereyeofthebeholdereyeofthebeholdereyeofthebeho
ldereyeofthebeholdereyeofthebeholdereyeofthebeholdereyeofthebehol
dereyeofthebeholdereyeofthebeholdereyeofthebeholdereyeofthebehold
ereyeofthebeholdereyeofthebeholdereyeofthebeholdereyeofthebeholde
reyeofthebeholdereyeofthebeholdereyeofthebeholdereyeofthebeholder
eyeofthebeholdereyeofthebeholdereyeofthebeholdereyeofthebeholdere
yeofthebeholdereyeofthebeholdereyeofthebeholdereyeofthebeholderey
eofthebeholdereyeofthebeholdereyeofthebeholdereyeofthebeholdereye
ofthebeholdereyeofthebeholdereyeofthebeholdereyeofthebeholdereyeo
fthebeholdereyeofthebeholdereyeofthebeholdereyeofthebeholdereyeof
thebeholdereyeofthebeholdereyeofthebeholdereyeofthebeholdereyeoft
hebeholdereyeofthebeholdereyeofthebeholdereyeofthebeholdereyeofth
ebeholdereyeofthebeholdereyeofthebeholdereyeofthebeholdereyeofthe
beholdereyeofthebeholdereyeofthebeholdereyeofthebeholdereyeoftheb
eholdereyeofthebeholdereyeofthebeholdereyeofthebeholdereyeofthebe
holdereyeofthebeholdereyeofthebeholdereyeofthebeholdereyeofthebeh
oldereyeofthebeholdereyeofthebeholdereyeofthebeholdereyeofthebeho
ldereyeofthebeholdereyeofthebeholdereyeofthebeholdereyeofthebehol
dereyeofthebeholdereyeofthebeholdereyeofthebeholdereyeofthebehold
ereyeofthebeholdereyeofthebeholdereyeofthebeholdereyeofthebeholde
reyeofthebeholdereyeofthebeholdereyeofthebeholdereyeofthebeholder
eyeofthebeholdereyeofthebeholdereyeofthebeholdereyeofthebeholdere
yeofthebeholdereyeofthebeholdereyeofthebeholdereyeofthebeholderey
eofthebeholdereyeofthebeholdereyeofthebeholdereyeofthebeholdereye
ofthebeholdereyeofthebeholdereyeofthebeholdereyeofthebeholdereyeo
fthebeholdereyeofthebeholdereyeofthebeholdereyeofthebeholdereyeof
thebeholdereyeofthebeholdereyeofthebeholdereyeofthebeholdereyeoft
hebeholdereyeofthebeholdereyeofthebeholdereyeofthebeholdereyeofth
ebeholdereyeofthebeholdereyeofthebeholdereyeofthebeholdereyeofthe

XIX. Divine Photography, Artwork & Illustration

The imagination is the cradle where pleasures are born.

~~~Marquis de Sade

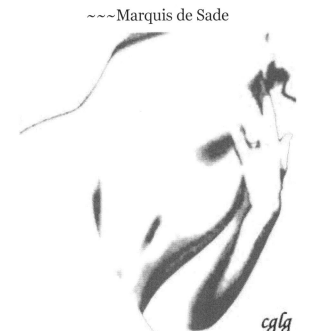

Artist CGLGArtwork featured at: www.eroticalee.com

www.eroticalee.com:

I am in awe of the creative ability one must have to use a camera or a paint brush or a pencil, and design exactly what a person's sexual psyche desires to be visualized.

I truly respect, admire and appreciate each artist and every website in which these creative works are featured.

Without these lustful, exotic explanations of sexual expression, the words in my book or any book, for that matter, would be without foundation.

When I discovered the magnificent and erotic artwork and photography that is featured at www.eroticalee.com, I could not find enough places in my book to show-off their carnal creativity.

What inspired me most about this website is the artwork and photography in which so many wedding rings were portrayed as the centerpiece of Erotica, conveying to the viewer absolute proof of everlasting entwined lust and loyalty, that is capable within monogamous devotion.

I encourage you to spend a lot of time viewing the artwork and photography at www.eroticalee.com. It celebrates everything that is beautiful about the female body... shows all that is enjoyable about giving oral sex to your man... and objectifies the sweet lust of wedded love.

www.Gradiva.com:

Artist Kathryn Hitt of the San Francisco Bay Area and Artist "EL STABO" of New York City, are only two of the outstanding, brilliant artists featured here. There is so much exceptional artwork on this website, that I had a difficulty choosing which pieces would best fit the tone of my book.

www.Gradiva.com has illustrations, drawings and artwork that celebrate everything that is wicked, nasty lustful and erotic. This is the website to visit if you want to send your man a naughtily suggestive postcard or if you want to add a sexy illustration or drawing to something you've created for him, to spice-up your romantic relationship.

www.secretgardenpublishing.com:

Much of the artwork and most of the sketched illustrations featured in my book can be found here. This website is dedicated to the sensual splendor of sacred sex and the profound intimacy of devoted lovemaking.

If you are interested in learning more about the spirituality of sex and how you can gain the skill and knowledge to obtain a deeper, sweeter connection with your man through sex, than I encourage you to explore all the exclusive information, as well as the many wonderful products available at www.secretgardenpublishing.com.

All of the photographs that I found at the websites www.sexual-compare.com, www.adultcheck.com, www.assnewcumers.com, take pornography to a level of much-needed sexual education.

If you need or want more visualization in regard to the Male Sex Organ or on the act of Anal Sex, please visit these sexually-explicit/ educational websites for a multitude of photographs which better illustrate and educate about the Male Sex Organ and on the act of Anal Sex, through imagery.

It is often much easier to understand or to re-enact something that you've seen, rather-than on what you've only read?

Many readers judge the power of a book
by the shock it gives their feelings.

~~~Henry Wadsworth Longfellow

Artwork featured at: www.gradiva.com

researchreadrecognizeresearchreadrecognizeresearchreadrecognizere
searchreadrecognizeresearchreadrecognizeresearchreadrecognizerese
archreadrecognizeresearchreadrecognizeresearchreadrecognizeresear
chreadrecognizeresearchreadrecognizeresearchreadrecognizeresearch
readrecognizeresearchreadrecognizeresearchreadrecognizeresearchre
adrecognizeresearchreadrecognizeresearchreadrecognizeresearchread
recognizeresearchreadrecognizeresearchreadrecognizeresearchreadre
cognizeresearchreadrecognizeresearchreadrecognizeresearchreadreco
gnizeresearchreadrecognizeresearchreadrecognizeresearchreadrecogn
izeresearchreadrecognizeresearchreadrecognizeresearchreadrecogniz
eresearchreadrecognizeresearchreadrecognizeresearchreadrecognizer
esearchreadrecognizeresearchreadrecognizeresearchreadrecognizeres
earchreadrecognizeresearchreadrecognizeresearchreadrecognizeresea
rchreadrecognizeresearchreadrecognizeresearchreadrecognizeresearc
hreadrecognizeresearchreadrecognizeresearchreadrecognizeresearchr
eadrecognizeresearchreadrecognizeresearchreadrecognizeresearchrea
drecognizeresearchreadrecognizeresearchreadrecognizeresearchreadr
ecognizeresearchreadrecognizeresearchreadrecognizeresearchreadrec
ognizeresearchreadrecognizeresearchreadrecognizeresearchreadrecog
nizeresearchreadrecognizeresearchreadrecognizeresearchreadrecogni
zeresearchreadrecognizeresearchreadrecognizeresearchreadrecognize

Where to Find 'It' on the Internet

researchreadrecognizeresearchreadrecognizeresearchreadrecognizere
searchreadrecognizeresearchreadrecognizeresearchreadrecognizerese
archreadrecognizeresearchreadrecognizeresearchreadrecognizeresear
chreadrecognizeresearchreadrecognizeresearchreadrecognizeresearch
readrecognizeresearchreadrecognizeresearchreadrecognizeresearchre
adrecognizeresearchreadrecognizeresearchreadrecognizeresearchread
recognizeresearchreadrecognizeresearchreadrecognizeresearchreadre
cognizeresearchreadrecognizeresearchreadrecognizeresearchreadreco
gnizeresearchreadrecognizeresearchreadrecognizeresearchreadrecogn
izeresearchreadrecognizeresearchreadrecognizeresearchreadrecogniz
eresearchreadrecognizeresearchreadrecognizeresearchreadrecognizer
esearchreadrecognizeresearchreadrecognizeresearchreadrecognizeres
earchreadrecognizeresearchreadrecognizeresearchreadrecognizeresea
rchreadrecognizeresearchreadrecognizeresearchreadrecognizeresearc
hreadrecognizeresearchreadrecognizeresearchreadrecognizeresearchr
eadrecognizeresearchreadrecognizeresearchreadrecognizeresearchrea
drecognizeresearchreadrecognizeresearchreadrecognizeresearchreadr
ecognizeresearchreadrecognizeresearchreadrecognizeresearchreadrec
ognizeresearchreadrecognizeresearchreadrecognizeresearchreadrecog
nizeresearchreadrecognizeresearchreadrecognizeresearchreadrecogni
zeresearchreadrecognizeresearchreadrecognizeresearchreadrecognize
researchreadrecognizeresearchreadrecognizeresearchreadrecognizere
searchreadrecognizeresearchreadrecognizeresearchreadrecognizerese
archreadrecognizeresearchreadrecognizeresearchreadrecognizeresear
chreadrecognizeresearchreadrecognizeresearchreadrecognizeresearch
readrecognizeresearchreadrecognizeresearchreadrecognizeresearchre
adrecognizeresearchreadrecognizeresearchreadrecognizeresearchread
recognizeresearchreadrecognizeresearchreadrecognizeresearchreadre
cognizeresearchreadrecognizeresearchreadrecognizeresearchreadreco
gnizeresearchreadrecognizeresearchreadrecognizeresearchreadrecogn
izeresearchreadrecognizeresearchreadrecognizeresearchreadrecogniz
eresearchreadrecognizeresearchreadrecognizeresearchreadrecognizer
esearchreadrecognizeresearchreadrecognizeresearchreadrecognizeres
earchreadrecognizeresearchreadrecognizeresearchreadrecognizeresea
rchreadrecognizeresearchreadrecognizeresearchreadrecognizeresearc

XX. Where to Find 'It' on the Internet

A

www.aboutmasturbation.com
www.adameve.com
www.adultcheck.com
www.adultdvdgold.com
www.adultsupermart.com
www.adulttoychest.com
www.afraidtoask.com
www.agentprovocateur.com
www.all-of-sex.com
www.allsexguide.com
www.alwaysuseaCondom.com
www.amazon.com
www.annasgourmet.com
www.anniesprinkle.com
www.anal-sex-information.com
www.analsexyes.com
www.arsrosa.com
www.articochef.com
www.ashleysextoys.com
www.assnewcumers.com
www.athenainstitute.com
www.a2zmasturbation.com
www.autumn-harvest.com
www.avacadell.com

B

www.babeland.com
www.babeland.com/sexinfo/howto/blow-job
www.barnesnoble.com
www.bbcamerica.com
www.beercollections.com
www.bedroombondage.com
www.bellaluxuries.com
www.bettydodson.com
www.bleachbum.com
www.blowfish.com
www.bodyperks.com
www.bombaycompany.com
www.bookbyyoupublishing.com
www.bostonmedicalgroup.com/pe_treatment. html

C

www.candlelighttoys.com
www.candycare.com
www.cajun-gifts.com

www.carlton.com
www.caviaretc.com
www.celestialproducts.com
www.censoredtoys.com
www.chocolatefantasies.com
www.clone-a-willy.com
www.condomania.com
www.creativec.yoll.net/rcharts.htm
www.curliegirl.com
www.cyberskinsextoys.com

D

www.dearlady.com
www.delightfuldeliveries.com
www.designityourselfgiftbaskets.com
www.docjohnson.com
www.dontspitswallow.com
www.dreamdresser.com
www.Drlust.com
www.drphil.com
www.drsusanblock.com

E

www.early2bed.com
www.edenfantasys.com
www.ehealthmd.com
www.electriqueboutique.com
www.epicureanfoods.com
www.emedicinehealth.com
www.emedicine.com
www.enchantmentsny.com
www.en.wikipedia.org/wiki/Premature_ejaculation
www.erectile-dysfunction-advisor.com
www.erectile-dysfunction-impotence.org
www.erectile-dysfunction-treatment.org
www.erecthard.com
www.eroticalee.com
www.eroticshopping.com
www.evesgarden.com
www.exalte.com
www.experts.about.com

F

www.faq-site.com
www.familydoctor.org
www.ffgc.com
www.findgift.com
www.Fn-Fun.Com
www.ForbiddenErotics.com

www.fredericks.com

G
www.girlshop.com
www.giveashare.com
www.goddesslife.com
www.goodfood2u.com
www.goodvibrations.com
www.gradiva.com

H
www.hammacherschlemmer.com
www.handJobAdvice.com
www.harryanddavid.com
www.health-nexus.com/premature_ejaculation11.htm
www.holisticwisdom.com
www.holisticwisdom.com
www.howtogivehead.biz
www.howtosuckacock.com

I
www.icecreamsource.com
www.impotence.org
www.impotent.com
www.instantsexyletters.com
www.intimatesynergy.com
www.intlgourmet.com
www.isabellehutton.com
www.iysextoys.com

J
www.jahsonic.com
www.janesguide.com
www.jasonschock.com

K
www.kamashop.com
www.kama-sutra-free.com
www.keepitkinky.co.uk
www.kinglove.com

L
www.laperla.com
www.LiberatorShapes.com
www.libida.com
www.littlebluebottle.com
www.loversemporium.co.uk
www.luckysextoys.com
www.LunarLandOwner.com
www.lustique.com

M
www.massage-tools.com

www.masqueradebooks.com
www.Mioplex.com
www.menagerieroweintlinc.com
www.myprivatetoybox.com
www.mypleasure.com
www.montenapoleone.com
www.mightyflirt.com
www.macys.com
www.mydavinci.com
www.malehealthcenter.com
www.menshealth.com
www.masturbation-techniques.net
www.malehealthcenter.com
www.maxoderm-enhancement-system.com
N
www.naughtynovelty.zoovy.com
www.newthoughtkabbalah.com
O
www.overstock.com
P
www.pabo.com
www.pancakeshop.com
www.paramountcaviar.com
www.Partygals.com
www.PassionShops.com
www.penishealth.com
www.penis-website.com/penis.html
www.playboy.com
www.pleasurenight.com
www.plumparty.com
www.my-penis.org
www.puckerup.com
www.purelyamerican.com
www.polecatsdvd.com
www.poledanzer.com
www.pornstarclothing.com
R
www.ratemycock.com
www.redenvelope.com
www.romancewrestling.com
S
www.sabbiarosa.com
www.sacredsexsecrets.com
www.salon.com
www.satisfactiondirect.co.uk
www.screamkreem.com

www.secretgardenpublishing.com
www.sediva.com
www.seekingo.com
www.sensualseductress.com
www.senso.com
www.sexeditorials.com/masturbation/female
www.sextutor.com
www.sex-superstore.com
www.sexual-compare.com
www.sexuality.org
www.sexy-lingerie.uk.com
www.shopinprivate.com
www.sinfulplaythings.com
www.simplyshe.com
www.signaturedays.com
www.SpicyGear.com
www.sportsheets.com
www.spoylt.com
www.stayerect.com
www.starwishing.com
www.steelsgourmet.com
www.stockroom.com
www.store.playboy.com
www.stormyleather.com
T
www.tantra-sex.com
www.the-penis.com
www.thingsYouNeverKnewExisted.com
www.toyssexshop.com
www.tracycabot.com
www.trashy.com
www.travelbasketsinc.com
V
www.viamontenapoleone.org
www.vibrel.com
www.victoriassecret.com
W
www.winecountrygiftbaskets.com
www.writesong4you.com
www.wvgourmetfoods.com
X
www.Xandria.com
www.xperiencedays.com

getscrewedgetlaidgetfuckedgetscrewedgetlaidgetfuckedgetscrewedget
laidgetfuckedgetscrewedgetlaidgetfuckedgetscrewedgetlaidgetfucked
getscrewedgetlaidgetfuckedgetscrewedgetlaidgetfuckedgetscrewedget
laidgetfuckedgetscrewedgetlaidgetfuckedgetscrewedgetlaidgetfucked
getscrewedgetlaidgetfuckedgetscrewedgetlaidgetfuckedgetscrewedget
laidgetfuckedgetscrewedgetlaidgetfuckedgetscrewedgetlaidgetfucked
getscrewedgetlaidgetfuckedgetscrewedgetlaidgetfuckedgetscrewedget
laidgetfuckedgetscrewedgetlaidgetfuckedgetscrewedgetlaidgetfucked
getscrewedgetlaidgetfuckedgetscrewedgetlaidgetfuckedgetscrewedget
laidgetfuckedgetscrewedgetlaidgetfuckedgetscrewedgetlaidgetfucked
getscrewedgetlaidgetfuckedgetscrewedgetlaidgetfuckedgetscrewedget
laidgetfuckedgetscrewedgetlaidgetfuckedgetscrewedgetlaidgetfucked
getscrewedgetlaidgetfuckedgetscrewedgetlaidgetfuckedgetscrewedget
laidgetfuckedgetscrewedgetlaidgetfuckedgetscrewedgetlaidgetfucked
getscrewedgetlaidgetfuckedgetscrewedgetlaidgetfuckedgetscrewedget
laidgetfuckedgetscrewedgetlaidgetfuckedgetscrewedgetlaidgetfucked

Last Word

getscrewedgetlaidgetfuckedgetscrewedgetlaidgetfuckedgetscrewedget
laidgetfuckedgetscrewedgetlaidgetfuckedgetscrewedgetlaidgetfucked
getscrewedgetlaidgetfuckedgetscrewedgetlaidgetfuckedgetscrewedget
laidgetfuckedgetscrewedgetlaidgetfuckedgetscrewedgetlaidgetfucked
getscrewedgetlaidgetfuckedgetscrewedgetlaidgetfuckedgetscrewedget
laidgetfuckedgetscrewedgetlaidgetfuckedgetscrewedgetlaidgetfucked
getscrewedgetlaidgetfuckedgetscrewedgetlaidgetfuckedgetscrewedget
laidgetfuckedgetscrewedgetlaidgetfuckedgetscrewedgetlaidgetfucked
getscrewedgetlaidgetfuckedgetscrewedgetlaidgetfuckedgetscrewedget
laidgetfuckedgetscrewedgetlaidgetfuckedgetscrewedgetlaidgetfucked
getscrewedgetlaidgetfuckedgetscrewedgetlaidgetfuckedgetscrewedget
laidgetfuckedgetscrewedgetlaidgetfuckedgetscrewedgetlaidgetfucked
getscrewedgetlaidgetfuckedgetscrewedgetlaidgetfuckedgetscrewedget
laidgetfuckedgetscrewedgetlaidgetfuckedgetscrewedgetlaidgetfucked
getscrewedgetlaidgetfuckedgetscrewedgetlaidgetfuckedgetscrewedget
laidgetfuckedgetscrewedgetlaidgetfuckedgetscrewedgetlaidgetfucked
getscrewedgetlaidgetfuckedgetscrewedgetlaidgetfuckedgetscrewedget
laidgetfuckedgetscrewedgetlaidgetfuckedgetscrewedgetlaidgetfucked
getscrewedgetlaidgetfuckedgetscrewedgetlaidgetfuckedgetscrewedget
laidgetfuckedgetscrewedgetlaidgetfuckedgetscrewedgetlaidgetfucked
getscrewedgetlaidgetfuckedgetscrewedgetlaidgetfuckedgetscrewedget
laidgetfuckedgetscrewedgetlaidgetfuckedgetscrewedgetlaidgetfucked
getscrewedgetlaidgetfuckedgetscrewedgetlaidgetfuckedgetscrewedget
laidgetfuckedgetscrewedgetlaidgetfuckedgetscrewedgetlaidgetfucked
getscrewedgetlaidgetfuckedgetscrewedgetlaidgetfuckedgetscrewedget
laidgetfuckedgetscrewedgetlaidgetfuckedgetscrewedgetlaidgetfucked
getscrewedgetlaidgetfuckedgetscrewedgetlaidgetfuckedgetscrewedget
laidgetfuckedgetscrewedgetlaidgetfuckedgetscrewedgetlaidgetfucked
getscrewedgetlaidgetfuckedgetscrewedgetlaidgetfuckedgetscrewedget
laidgetfuckedgetscrewedgetlaidgetfuckedgetscrewedgetlaidgetfucked
getscrewedgetlaidgetfuckedgetscrewedgetlaidgetfuckedgetscrewedget
laidgetfuckedgetscrewedgetlaidgetfuckedgetscrewedgetlaidgetfucked
getscrewedgetlaidgetfuckedgetscrewedgetlaidgetfuckedgetscrewedget
laidgetfuckedgetscrewedgetlaidgetfuckedgetscrewedgetlaidgetfucked
getscrewedgetlaidgetfuckedgetscrewedgetlaidgetfuckedgetscrewedget
laidgetfuckedgetscrewedgetlaidgetfuckedgetscrewedgetlaidgetfucked

XXI. Last Word

Eroticism is first a search for pleasure,
and the goal of techniques of love is to
attain the divine state, which is infinite delight.

~~~Kama Sutra

Artwork featured at: www.gradiva.com

Before you ever have sex with your man again, you need to make sure that you've fully processed everything that you've read in this book.

If you have a computer, you know how slow it can become when too much unused and unneeded information bogs down the hard drive. The only way your computer will become more speedy and better productive, is when you make the effort and take the time to delete and dump any and all unused and unneeded information and re-format, if necessary.

Your brain is much sharper and much more productive than your computer. Over the years, you have allowed too much mis-information and too many wrongly subjective ideas about men and sex, to bog down your sexual intellect.

If you truly desire a successful romantic relationship with your man, then you must mentally delete all the misinformation and wrongfully subjective ideas that you once believed you knew about men and sex.

That is the *only way* that you will ever have what you want with him.

Ever.

Nannette LaRee Hernandez

How to Really Love a Man

Walk his dog *Listen to his opinion first* *Send him flowers* *Take the advice you've asked him for* *Arrange a Romantic Evening just for him: two tickets to a hockey game, hot dogs & beer* *Kiss him when you ask him to take out the trash* *Put away his tools after you've used them* *Let him parent the kids his way and not your way* *Give him Love Notes* *Make an effort to compliment him on what he does and try not to complain so much about what he rarely does* *Be a Creative Lover* *Tell him often that he makes you happy* *Thank him for doing such a great job* *Be considerate when he wants to spend time with his buddies* *Don't ask him if he thinks you look too fat* *Be satisfied that you have a man who took the time to buy you such a thoughtful gift* *Tell him often that he is the sexiest man in the World* *Explain to him what you want-don't expect him to just know* *Wear sexy lingerie* *Take him out to his favorite restaurant-the one that gives you heartburn* *Don't continually ask him how he is feeling* *Don't throw out his High School Basketball Team T-Shirt, no matter how ragged it is* *Rub his neck on a long drive* *Don't roll your eyes when he plays with the X-Box* *Accept him for who is and where he is at and not for how you personally think he can improve himself * *Remind him how clever he is* *Give him a massage that leads to sex* *Hint that when he hits the laundry basket and puts down the toilet seat, it makes you want to kiss him all over* *Tell him every day how very much you love him*

How to Really Fuck a Man

Wear red thigh-high stockings and a faux pearl necklace to bed *sex him Brazilian-style* *serve him pizza and beer then give him a naked lap dance* *lightly caress his cock under the kitchen table with your toes or the ball of your foot* *ask him to join you in a midnight bubble bath: wash his hair, massage his neck and shoulders then stroke his cock until he cums* *read to him from 'Letters to Penthouse'* *ask him to cum in your face* *do some sex-research then teach him to become multi-orgasmic* *run your hand down the curve of his ass while he's shaving* *text-message him something naughty* *buy him a membership to a good Internet porn site for his birthday* *host a big-girl 'slumber party' with lingerie, naughty toys and sexy accessories* *buy at least two new things for a private play date with him in the bedroom* *dance your tongue down the bridge from his balls to his ass* *buy a long masquerade feather and sweep it all over his body as he is about to fall asleep* *feed him chocolate-dipped strawberries and Champagne on a nothing-special Tuesday night* *lick his earlobes when he's fucking you Missionary* *purchase a red light and purple satin sheets and turn your bedroom into a brothel for the evening* *give him Head before he heads out the door for poker night with his buddies* *do that sex trick you used to do with him when you first started dating him* *tell him every day what a passionate, sexy man he is.

Authoress Nannette LaRee Hernandez lives in St. Joseph, Michigan. Her original book, 'Creative Screwing: a woman's guide to becoming an erotic enchantress of superlustful sex ' has sold over 300,000 copies. She has written several E-books and hosts her own "Sensual Seductress" seminars. You can contact Nannette LaRee at Seshat65@yahoo.com or at her website www.sensualSeductress.com

Made in the USA
San Bernardino, CA
12 March 2014